Mills & Boon
Best Seller Romance

A chance to read and collect some of the best-loved novels
from Mills & Boon—the world's largest publisher of
romantic fiction.

Every month, six titles by favourite Mills & Boon authors
will be re-published in the *Best Seller Romance* series.

A list of other titles in the *Best Seller Romance* series
can be found at the end of this book.

Kay Thorpe

LORD OF
LA PAMPA

MILLS & BOON LIMITED
LONDON·TORONTO

First published 1977
Australian copyright 1983
Philippine copyright 1978
This edition 1983

© Kay Thorpe 1977

ISBN 0 263 74493 0

Set in Linotype Granjon 10 on 11 pt.
02–1183

Made and printed in Great Britain by
Richard Clay (The Chaucer Press) Ltd,
Bungay, Suffolk

CHAPTER ONE

The Argentinian had spoken in Spanish, but his meaning bridged the language gap in a manner Lian could not fail to comprehend. Pushing away the untouched drink in front of her, she shook her head and got to her feet, smoothing down the skirt of the figure-hugging black dress with hands gone suddenly nerveless.

'No,' she said stumblingly, 'nada más. Discúlpeme, señor.'

He had risen with her, face registering puzzlement rather than anger. 'Qué pasa?' he said on a rising inflection. 'No comprendo.'

Heads were turning towards them at neighbouring tables, interest aroused by the sight of the slender young English girl with her smooth, shining bell of ashen hair. Lian caught the eye of the man seated behind and to one side of her own table companion, and flushed under the sardonic gaze. It was obvious what he was thinking: the same thing this man opposite had thought. What kind of a fool was she not to have realised what kind of place this was and what would be expected of her! She wasn't at home in London now. This was Buenos Aires, a foreign city in a foreign land. She had never felt so utterly alone as she did at this moment.

'Siéntese, por favor,' the Argentinian urged, indicating the seat she had just vacated, and then in a lower tone, 'Cuánto vale?'

Lian sought for the words to tell him he was in error and couldn't find ones adequate to the occasion. Phrase-books just didn't cater for this sort of thing, she acknowledged on an edge of hysteria. She could, she supposed, simply turn round

and walk away from him, only she somehow doubted if it
would be as easy as that. Drawn once more by the gaze of the
man seated at the next table, she took a deep slow breath
before asking:

'*Habla usted inglés?*'

'Yes,' he said in excellent though heavily accented English,
and one black eyebrow lifted. 'You wish me to interpret for
you?'

She shook her head, wishing herself anywhere but in this
spot. 'I'd be very grateful if you would just explain to him
that I'm not ... not available in the way he thinks I am.
There's been a mistake.'

The brow lifted still further. 'You work here at the club,
do you not?'

'Yes. Yes, I do.' She was hot with embarrassment. 'But
not in that capacity. Please, *señor* ...' She let the rest of the
sentence trail away, realising that they had the attention of
most of their immediate neighbours by now. With sinking
heart she saw the club proprietor starting across the crowded,
smoke-hazed room towards them, drawn no doubt by the
faint disturbance. He was still the same fat, balding Latin
to whom she had been so grateful for his offer of a job, so
why did she see him now in such a different light? She knew
the answer to that one, of course. He had known what he was
letting her in for, if she hadn't. In all probability he had
taken it for granted that she had no objections to extending
her duties as hostess to cover all aspects of clientele enter-
tainment. It was her own ridiculous naïveté which had
brought her to such a situation.

The man at the other table gave a slight shrug as if in
somewhat disbelieving acceptance, and addressed her companion in Spanish too quickly and fluently spoken for her to
grasp more than a word here and there. He finished as the
proprietor reached them, leaving the other man looking suddenly and uncomfortably aware of some misunderstanding,
to speak to the newcomer with a curt familiarity which

reduced him to smarmy grovelling in seconds.

'*Perdóneme*, Señor Mendoza,' he begged. Ignoring the man on the far side of the table, he took Lian by the arm and urged her across to the new one, pressing her down into a seat with further expressions of regret and apology and leaving her there while he turned back to dismiss her erstwhile companion.

Somewhat dazedly Lian met the dark eyes regarding her at the moment with unconcealed contempt. It was not a reassuring face, features tautly etched, in alien olive beneath a ruthlessly smoothed head of jet black hair. He was wearing a white tuxedo which emphasised his breadth of shoulder, the shirt under it almost certainly silk. A tall, lean man with power both in him and about him. He frightened her a little.

'I don't know just what you said to him,' she got out, 'but thank you for coming to my rescue.'

The brief incline of his head was satirical. 'If you did not like the look of the man you should not have accepted his companionship in the first place.'

Her grimace was wry. 'He seemed pleasant enough, and that happens to be my job – or at least, I thought it was.'

'You are trying to say you were not aware of the—demands, shall we say, of your position here?' He sounded sceptical, for which in retrospect, Lian could hardly blame him. 'You are newly arrived in Argentina, perhaps?'

'Fairly,' she admitted. She gave him a level green look. 'I daresay that's no excuse for stupidity, but I genuinely believed the job was just to sit with the customers and be friendly. Where I come from it usually is.'

There was no appreciable change in his expression. 'You have done such work before in your own country?'

'Once. But the club I was employed in had strict rules about hostesses not mixing with customers off the premises.'

White teeth showed momentarily as his mouth pulled into a faint smile. 'Here too they have such a rule. There are private rooms on the upper floor for the purpose.'

'Oh, lord!' She put her hands to her hot cheeks, unable to meet the mocking scrutiny. 'I should have realised it was just too good to be true! A job with accommodation seemed like manna from heaven the way I was fixed. I really——' She paused as a sudden thought struck her, lifting her head to look at him again. 'May I ask what it was you did say to those two, *señor?*' she requested with some hesitation.

'Certainly.' The amusement had grown, though still allied to a certain contempt. 'I told them both I had already bought your time for the night.'

'You did what?' She was stunned and disbelieving. 'You —You *couldn't* have!'

'It was the only way to save trouble. Rios would not have been pleased had you rejected a customer for no reason at all. Tomorrow he will want his share of the fee you will have earned tonight.'

Lian bit her lip. She was out of the frying pan into the fire, it seemed, and she wasn't at all sure how to handle the situation.

'I shan't be here tomorrow,' she said at last. 'In fact, I'm leaving right now.'

'No, you are not,' he came back quietly as she made to push back her chair. 'You are going to continue to sit where you are until I say it is time to go—unless you would prefer that I call Rios over again and have him convince you?' He watched her sink slowly down into the chair again and nodded. 'Good. Now you are showing sense.'

Lian said with spirit, 'Look, Señor'—she cast her mind back —'Mendoza, I realise I've been all kinds of a fool, but there's no way you're going to get me to spend any more time with you than I want to. No one can stop me leaving this place!'

'You think not?' He was unmoved by the outburst. 'You have a lot to learn about the ways of such men as Rios. He has taken you on his payroll, he will expect suitable return.

Should it be denied him he may find other ways of extracting a profit. You have heard of the white slave traffic?'

She made a small sound of protest and attempted ridicule. 'You're just trying to scare me!'

'Perhaps a little. You deserve to be frightened. But the market exists none the less, and an English girl of your colouring and looks would fetch a handsome price.' The dark regard was pitiless. 'You still wish to leave?'

Lian shook her head, not wanting to believe him, not daring not to. 'Please,' she entreated in a small voice. 'I'm not what you think. I—I was stranded and desperate when I took this job. There was nothing else I could do.'

'So?' He took out a gold cigarette case and extracted a slim cheroot, placing it between his lips and thumbing the table lighter into flame. The smoke wreathed fragrantly between them for a moment before he added, 'You had better tell me the whole story, I think. When did you first come to Buenos Aires?'

'Yesterday.' She sensed his surprise and hurried on, 'You see, I was supposed to join up with a dancing troupe appearing right here at the Club Rios, only when I got here they'd already gone on to Porto Alegre. The agency must have got the dates wrong.'

'Could you not have followed them to Porto?'

'I hadn't enough money on me to do it under my own steam, and I haven't been able to contact the agency in London by phone yet.'

It was difficult to read his reactions. 'You have been to the Consulate?'

'I tried today, but it was closed for the weekend. I didn't have the money to spend any more nights in a hotel, so when Rios offered me a job as hostess here in the club and a room to go with it I jumped at it. As I said, I should have known better.'

'Yes, you should.' He was studying her with an odd look

in his eyes. 'So, you are a dancer. Are you a good dancer?'

'I like to think so. Good enough, anyway, to get the chance to come out here to South America.'

The smile was brief and cynical. 'Your troupe, they are all blonde-haired?'

'Well, yes, I believe so.'

'Then the dancing is of little consequence.'

'I don't think I understand what you're getting at.'

'What I am getting at, as you so gracefully put it, is that my countrymen would be drawn by the spectacle alone regardless of the standard of talent, and pay accordingly. The natural blonde is rare in our part of the world.'

Lian had sparks in her eyes. 'I *can* dance, *señor*.'

'I have no doubt of it. But not, I think, in any troupe of high repute. I saw the Bluebell Girls in Rio, some time ago. They are both beautiful *and* talented. You have not been invited to join them?'

'I'm not tall enough to make the Bluebells.' She held his gaze for a long moment, then gave a sudden sigh. 'All right, so I'm probably not in that league. This seemed like my big chance and I took it with both hands. It isn't my fault that the agency sent me to the wrong place.'

'The right place but the wrong time,' he corrected. 'You were to replace someone?'

'Yes, one of the girls had to fly home after a bad fall. They'll be one short in the routines now—though from what you say that won't really matter, will it?'

'Do not take that tone with me,' he said. 'The truth is painful but no excuse for sarcasm. You are not at home in England now.'

Lian bit back the sharp rejoinder which sprang to her lips. He was right, she wasn't. And at this particular moment she was in no position to antagonise the man any further. An apology went against the grain too, though, so she kept silent, resentment in the line of her chin.

'You learn quickly,' he said. 'Not a bad sign.' He paused

before adding on a different note, 'Did your family not object to your travelling so far alone?'

'I don't have any family,' she said. 'I was brought up in an orphanage.' Her voice firmed afresh. 'I'm twenty-two years old and quite capable of travelling alone. I've been doing it for years.'

'But never before so far,' he came back dryly. 'In ten or eleven years' time when you are my age you may have learned that independence gains little for the female.'

'In ten or eleven years' time I'll be past caring either way,' she retorted. Her glance went once more around the dimly lit room with its closely packed tables and heavily ornate décor. There was a group playing Latin-American music for the benefit of those crowding the dance floor, the sound barely rising above the babble of voices. Here and there she could see her fellow hostesses sitting with lone men at various tables. Even as she looked, she saw one raven-haired girl perhaps a year or so her senior rise and take her companion by the hand with a smiling gesture towards the staircase at the far end of the room. When she turned back to her own table there was warmth under her skin.

'You are convinced at last?' queried the man opposite. 'You believe what I tell you?'

'Part of it.' She made herself look at him. 'I still think I could walk out of here quite safely if I put my mind to it.'

He shrugged. 'And if you did, where would you go? By your own admittance you have little money, and hotels are expensive.'

'I have enough for tonight. Perhaps even for tomorrow night too, if I can find one a little less expensive. There must be some.'

'There are plenty, but not for any woman unprotected.' He sounded impatient. 'The problem will be resolved when the time comes. Until then you will pay me the compliment of appearing to enjoy my company.' One lean brown hand came out to crush the remains of the cheroot into a tray. 'Come, we will dance before I order drinks.'

Lian didn't move. 'Señor Mendoza,' she began on an edge of desperation, 'I didn't seem to be getting it through to you that I'm not prepared to accept your protection on those terms, any more than I'm prepared to stay here and work for Rios. I am going now to pack my things and then to leave. If anyone tries to stop me I shall start yelling for the police.'

'Then you had better start doing so now,' he said, 'because I am going to stop you.' He waited, mouth widening mirthlessly when she failed to rise. 'You are wise not to defy me. We will dance as I said.'

He was taller even than she had thought when he stood up, body tapering to waist and hips, with a look of sleek muscularity in the long line of his legs under the black trousers. When he took hold of her on the floor, she was conscious of strength in the grip of his hands, along with a surprising roughness where his palm touched the bare skin of her back— callouses, she imagined, from the feel, a hard ridge of them running along the base of the fingers. She wondered what could have caused them. Not manual labour, that was for certain. This man was used to commanding, not serving.

'You have not yet told me your name,' he said close to her ear as they moved to the rumba rhythm. 'What is it?'

'It's Lian,' she said. 'Lian Trevor.'

He said the name over, approval in his voice. 'An unusual name for an English girl, but attractive. I am Ricardo Mendoza.'

'How do you do.' She heard the dangerous little quiver in her voice and threw off all pretence at lightness. 'Please, can't we stop this—this charade? I'd welcome your help, Señor Mendoza, but not——'

'But not at the price you are so sure I am going to demand,' he finished for her as she hesitated. 'Did it occur to you that I might not find your English charms quite so irresistible as your previous companion? I prefer a woman who is warm and responsive, not cold like ice!'

Involuntarily she had stiffened. 'Then why have you been keeping me with you?' she asked.

'Because it happens to be the only way in which I can be of assistance to you. You appealed to me for help initially, and by granting it I made myself responsible for you.' The hand at her back was hard. 'I did not at any time suggest a personal interest in spending the night with you—that was a product of your own imagination. Perhaps it would teach you a much-needed lesson were I to make you carry through the duties to which I am entitled. Rios would be more than happy to accommodate me.'

'I'm sorry.' Her voice was low. 'I—I misunderstood.'

'Yes, you did. But not any more. You said you would welcome my help, and you shall have it, but only at the price of doing exactly as I say. Is that agreed?'

'Yes.' The doubts were still there at the back of her mind, yet she had to trust him; there seemed little alternative. 'What do you suggest?'

'Later.' His hand rested lightly against her hip for a moment as the rhythm altered. 'You respond well to our music. You find it strikes a chord within you?'

'I suppose it does. It's the kind of rhythm that makes you want to move to it.' She paused before tagging on, 'You dance well yourself, señor.'

He acknowledged the compliment with a brief inclination of his head. 'It is bred in the Latin. And you must call me Ricardo.'

She would have preferred to stick to the Señor; it seemed safer somehow. But for better or worse she had placed herself in his hands. 'Very well—Ricardo,' she said, and hoped her voice did not betray her trepidation.

'Tell me,' he said. 'If you are offered the choice between returning home and joining your fellow artists, which will you take?'

'I doubt if there'll be any question of a choice,' she returned. 'I signed a contract to complete the remaining six weeks of the tour. They're hardly likely to advance me my fare home simply because none of it is turning out to be quite what I expected.' She gave a small sigh. 'Anyway, I've nothing to go back to. The only reason I took that job as a hostess in London was because I couldn't find anything else I could do which paid enough to live on. I can't type or book-keep, or anything of that nature.'

'Did the orphanage not provide you with the means of earning your living in a more orthodox fashion?'

'They tried to. I had a flair for cookery, so they found me a job in a hotel restaurant near to the home when I was sixteen. I was supposed to learn all about catering, but all I did do was tidy up for the kitchen staff and run errands. I left as soon as I was eighteen and took a job as an au-pair with a family in Croydon until I could find an opening.' She stopped there in sudden discomfiture. 'I'm sorry—you can't possibly want to hear my whole life story.'

'On the contrary, that is just what I do want.' His regard was enigmatic. 'You were unhappy in this home as a child?'

'Oh no. It was a very good home, and none of us lacked for affection. They even let me take dancing lessons.'

'But not with a view to making a career in that line.'

'No.' Lian smiled a little. 'I remember once asking if I could audition for a part in the local theatre's pantomime when I was about fifteen—they used to use local children in the chorus. Matron was horrified at the thought of any of her children even contemplating going on the professional stage.'

'But they did allow you to use your talent occasionally?'

'Oh yes. I was the star turn at our own concerts. I can't really blame Matron for feeling the way she did. It was her job to send her charges out into respectable occupations with a secure income. Only I couldn't stand the thought of spending the best years of my life working in some dull respectable job.'

'You might have found a husband who would have taken you away from it,' Ricardo said lightly. 'Or would you regard marriage too as dull and respectable?'

'I don't know. I suppose it would have depended on the kind of man I married.'

'You have never thought of marrying?'

'I've thought *about* it. I imagine all girls do at some time or other.' She laughed. 'At fourteen I thought it must be wonderful to marry somebody like Gene Kelly, the film star —only younger, of course. By nineteen I'd decided that my career must always come first. I'd been dancing profession- ally for just a week when I made that decision. I've never reversed it even when I've been between jobs—and that's been pretty often.'

'There must have been men who wished to be with you. You did not refuse all contact with them, I trust?'

'I've had boy-friends. No one serious.'

'No one waiting to hear from you back there in London?' he insisted with an emphasis she found vaguely disturbing.

'No.' She hesitated. 'Señor——'

'Ricardo.'

'Ricardo, then.' She lifted her face to look up into his, seeing the skin stretched taut over the high cheekbones with an odd little churning sensation inside her. 'Why are you asking me all these questions? It can't be of any importance to you what I think or feel.'

Dark brows lifted arrogantly. 'I will decide what is of importance to me. You would like to sit down again and take a drink now?'

Lian shook her head, fighting the impulse to cut and run from this man while she still had the chance. 'I'd rather know just what you intend doing with me,' she said with a firmness she was far from feeling. 'If you know Rios so well perhaps a word from you will be enough to convince him of his mistake.'

'I shall be speaking to Rios,' he agreed. 'If you do not wish to drink then you will go and get your luggage from your room while I wait for you. We will leave when you are ready.'

'To go where?'

He drew in an impatient breath. 'You were to do as I say, were you not?'

'Well, yes, but——'

'Then do it, and quickly. It gets late. You will be quite safe, I assure you.'

Lian allowed herself to be drawn from the floor by the pressure of his hand beneath her elbow. She felt confused and uncertain, and not a little suspicious, but what other recourse did she have? To stay on here at the club was obviously out of the question, even if Rios would allow it. All she could do was go along with her benefactor and hope to meet any further difficulties if and when they arose.

No one stopped her on the way upstairs to the room she had been given on the second floor. She looked at it now with new eyes, averting them from the silk-draped bed. A very high-class place of its kind, judging from the quality of the furnishings and décor. She supposed she should feel flattered in one way that she should be considered worthy of employment in it. She looked at her reflection in the huge mirror hung above the bedhead and gave a wry little smile. It was her colouring again, of course. The face beneath it was attractive, she knew, but surely not so remarkable. Someone should have warned her that fair hair and skin were a hazard, not an asset, in this part of the world.

The thought of the man waiting for her downstairs brought a swift return of worry. She would be safe, he had assured her, but how could she be sure of his word? He was a stranger, this Ricardo Mendoza, and not a man easily denied. For all she knew she was jumping straight out of one nasty situation into another. Yet for the moment there was nothing else she could do but trust him.

He was waiting at the foot of the curving wrought iron staircase when she finally went down with her suitcase in her hand. A click of his fingers brought one of the waiters hurrying over to take it from her and bear it across the outer doors ahead of them. Rios watched the two of them from the far side of the long, low room, his expression hard to define through the smoke-wreathed atmosphere. If he objected to Lian's removal, he was certainly making no move towards having her stopped.

They left from the rear of the premises, coming up into the hot darkness of a back street where a taxi already waited. Ricardo paid off the man who had carried her suitcase up, and got in after her, giving the driver the name of a hotel.

Lian kept to her own side of the rear seat, vitally aware of his presence in the darkness and almost grateful when they turned out of the back alley into the wide main thoroughfare still thronged with people and traffic. Lights flashed everywhere, dazzling in their multi-hued appeal. The blare of music from the radio up front filled her ears.

'What did you tell Rios?' she asked when she could no longer bear the tension.

He shrugged. 'I told him nothing. He was satisfied to allow you to go.'

Her glance came round to his face, garishly highlighted by the flashing signs outside. 'You—paid him money?'

'Of course. How else would he reconcile himself to the loss of such a potential income?' His tone was heavy with irony. 'Rios is a man who equates everything in terms of money. For you his demand was high.'

'But I can't pay you back,' she exclaimed despairingly. 'At least, not immediately. If you'll tell me just how much I owe you——'

'It is of no consequence.' The wave of his hand dismissed the subject. 'When we reach the hotel you will go straight to your room. Tomorrow there will be time to talk.'

'About what? You've done enough for me already. I can't impose on your time any further after tonight.'

'I do not abandon a responsibility when only half completed,' he said with the same arrogant intonation he had displayed in the club. 'You will not argue with me over this, or any other matter—unless you would prefer after all to remain with Rios?'

Lian wondered if he really would return her to the club if she refused to take heed of his warning. There was no way of knowing what he might be capable of given enough provocation. All things considered, she could not afford to take the risk.

'All right,' she sighed. 'You made your point. I'll do whatever you say.'

His smile mocked her. 'I shall ask nothing of you beyond your capabilities—if obedience itself is not already doing so. You find it difficult, you English women, to submit yourselves to the ruling of the male. Here, the females are taught from birth that man is their master. In return they gain our protection and regard. Is that such a bad exchange?'

'I don't know,' she said after a moment. 'I suppose it has to depend on the temperament of the people concerned. I was taught to acquire independence of others.'

'Because of the nature of your upbringing perhaps, the knowledge that the institution could only support you to a certain point in your life. You have been unfortunate in your lack of a family to provide individual care. A father would have quelled your rebellious streak a little, if not wholly.'

Lian had to smile. 'I suppose you think a husband would do that too?'

'If he were anything of a man he would stand none of your liberated nonsense, yes.' His mouth had an odd slant to it. 'Under the circumstances, however, perhaps I should be grateful that you are as you are.'

Her brows drew together. 'I don't understand.'

'You do not have to understand tonight. I said we will talk in the morning.' He sat forward as the car began to draw up. 'Leave everything to me.'

There was no other choice but to obey. Lian followed him

out of the car to stand blinking up at the brightly lit façade of the obviously luxury class hotel with the confusion growing deeper by the minute within her. Whatever he had in mind, she wasn't going to find out about it until the morning, so she might as well reconcile herself to it. But what would all this have cost him by then? And what kind of return was he going to expect?

The hotel was as sumptuous inside as out, the carpets thick underfoot, the décor modern but beautifully restrained. Conscious of the relative cheapness of the white stole she had thrown about her shoulders before leaving the Club Rios, Lian waited a little distance from the reception desk while Ricardo arranged a room for her, not really believing that it would be a separate one until she saw the key in the bellboy's hand.

They took the lift to the fifth floor in silence, following the dark blue uniformed figure along the beige-carpeted corridor to a door about two thirds of the way down. Ricardo came with her into the room, handing the boy a tip after he had lifted the suitcase on to the stand. Lian looked at the French grey wallpaper and red velvet drapes, at the stylish white furnishings and half acre of deep red carpet. The cost, she knew, was already far beyond her now.

'Your bathroom is through that door over there,' Ricardo said behind her. 'I would suggest you get a good night's sleep without too much delay.'

'Am I going to need it?' she asked without turning. 'To withstand the shock, I mean.'

'You think you are going to be shocked?' He sounded amused. 'Perhaps interested may prove the better word.'

She turned then, with a swift gesture of appeal. 'Please, don't leave me in suspense like this. You want something from me in return for all you're doing—you've made that obvious. Won't you tell me what it is?'

'At breakfast,' he said. 'I have to have time to consider all the implications myself before I make the final decision.

There is even a possibility that I may decide against asking anything of you, in which case our discussion will be of a different nature. In either case, you will not be left to fend for yourself.' He took a final glance about the room, then nodded. 'We will eat in my sitting room at eight-thirty. You can find your way to suite 734?'

'I expect so.' She was going to get no more out of him, no matter how she tried, that was for certain. 'Eight-thirty, then.'

His smile was perfunctory. 'Goodnight.'

She stayed gazing at the closed door for several minutes after he had gone trying to consider the various implications. He had denied any personal interest in her, so that would appear to preclude the most obvious request. Yet what other kind of interest *could* he have? She had no skills which might conceivably be useful to him, no connections of any kind. Just a lone English girl stranded in a foreign city. It didn't make sense.

CHAPTER TWO

Morning brought no decrease in trepidation. Awakening from a fitful sleep, Lian bathed and dressed in a state of alternating moods, choosing a simple linen dress in pale green as the farthest away from her slinky black of the previous night.

Suite 734 was two floors above her own. Knocking tentatively on the double cream doors, she wondered what Ricardo would have done had she chosen to leave the hotel early this morning without seeing him again. It was difficult to imagine that he would have let her get away with it easily, yet Buenos Aires was a huge city—one of the largest in the world. To find her again he would have had to comb it. Pity she hadn't thought of it before. She knew she was kidding herself, of course. All other things aside, she had to know what this was all about. It was imperative to her peace of mind.

He was up and dressed in a beige linen suite; the same man, yet with subtle differences from the night before. Breakfast had already been delivered, set on a table by the wide window with its panoramic views over the city. A chair stood ready on either side. Ricardo indicated one of them.

'You slept well?' he inquired as she sat.

'As well as can be expected,' she said. 'I had a lot on my mind.'

'I too,' he agreed. He took the chair opposite and shook out the pristine white napkin across his knees, helped himself to a roll from the basket after offering it across to her, and to a curl of butter still beaded with moisture from the overnight frosting. 'It occurred to me only bare moments ago that you might have preferred an English breakfast. Should you do so I can order it for you.'

'Just coffee and toast for me, thank you,' she denied. She drank from the deep white cup, watching his face over the rim and wishing he would say whatever he was going to say.

'You obviously don't live all the time in Buenos Aires,' she said at length when the pause had stretched to unbearable limits. 'Do you mind me asking which part of Argentina you do come from?'

'I come from the *pampas*,' he responded easily. 'The great plains some few hundred kilometres to the south.'

'Farming country?' she hazarded, thinking he looked anything but a farmer.

He smiled briefly. 'The Estancia Mendoza deals only in cattle. It supplies beef to all parts of the world.'

A ranch. She looked at him with fresh eyes, remembering the callouses on his hands. Reins, of course! He would use horses daily when at home. An Argentinian cattle baron! Small wonder he could treat money matters so casually. Some of them were reputed to be millionaires! She put down her cup with an unsteady hand.

'Did you make your decision?' she asked.

He touched the napkin to his lips before answering, eyes meeting hers across the width of the table. 'Yes,' he said. 'I did. I have a proposition to make to you.'

'Proposition?' She tried to sound cool and calm about it. 'Do you mean you want to offer me a job?'

'In a manner of speaking.' The pause was deliberate. 'How would you like to earn ten thousand of your pounds?'

Lian stared at him, her mind gone suddenly numb. 'I— Are you joking?'

'Not in the least. I wish to hire your services for six months. At the end of that time I will send you home to England and make arrangements to have that amount credited to your account at any bank you care to name.'

'My—services?'

The firmly chiselled mouth took on a sardonic slant. 'Not in the way you are thinking. I told you last night the kind of woman I prefer in my bed. You would have nothing to fear from me, no duties to perform. All I would want from you is your presence.'

There were faint green sparks in her eyes, a tinge of colour in her cheeks. 'That's very reassuring. May I ask exactly what my position in your household would be?'

'You would be my wife.' It was so quietly spoken it took a moment to penetrate. He held up a hand as she made to speak. 'You would be my wife, but only in name; and only for this period of six months.'

'And after that?' Lian felt dazed and more than a little bewildered. 'What would happen when the six months were up?'

'There would be an annulment. You would return home free of all entanglements, and with no need to work for your living.'

She shook her head slowly. 'I don't understand. Why——'

'I will explain. You will not interrupt while I do so.' He sat back in the chair, expression controlled, manner unhurried. 'To begin, I need go back some years to the time when my mother died and my father brought his other, illegitimate son to live on the *estancia* with us. Carlos is four years my junior, the child of a union between my father and a woman of the town for whom he formed an unreasonable attachment. When my father himself died some weeks ago, he left control of the *estancia* to the son who was first to be married, knowing that Carlos already planned to marry the daughter of our neighbour while I had no plans at all in that direction. I do not intend for Carlos to take my birthright from me. Need I say more?'

Lian drew in her breath long and slow in an attempt to sort out her spinning thoughts. 'Yes,' she got out, 'I'm afraid you need.'

'There is something I have not made clear?'

'Oh no, you've made it very clear. I understand your reasons for wanting a wife in such a hurry. I just can't quite grasp why you should be asking me to play the part. Surely one of your own countrywomen——'

'None of my own countrywomen would agree to the conditions I impose on the marriage. I have no wish to remain tied. It is merely a means to an end.'

'But why six months?'

'Because that is a condition my father imposed.' The smile held no humour. 'He knew me capable of finding a woman to fulfil the first, but held it unlikely that such a woman could be made to accept the terms.'

'You could have thwarted him altogether by finding a woman you wanted to keep as your wife,' she pointed out. 'There must be those who would *leap* at the opportunity to become the Señora Mendoza!'

Dark eyes glinted dangerously. 'One thing you must learn before we go further is to curb this inclination of yours towards sarcasm. I will have your respect.'

Her chin lifted. 'I haven't agreed to go any further. The whole idea is quite—preposterous!'

'For ten thousand pounds? Where else would you earn such a sum in six months?'

'I don't know.' She pressed back her chair with a sudden decisive movement. 'But the answer is no. I'll get what help I need from the Consulate.'

'Today is Sunday. It will not be open.' He hadn't moved, but there was something in his expression which stayed her. He eyed her for a long hard moment before adding softly, 'If you should attempt to leave this room without my permission I could telephone to Rios and have him collect you. He would be more than pleased to have you back.'

'You're just saying that to try and frighten me,' she retorted with more spirit than conviction. 'Rios has no power to take me back to that club of his against my will.'

'You think not?' He shrugged, reaching out for the instrument plugged in nearby and lifting the receiver. 'We shall see.'

Lian watched him dial one digit to obtain an outside line, and the first two of a number with a sense of unreality. This couldn't be happening to her. It simply couldn't! It was like something out of a dream—or a nightmare.

'Don't,' she said as his index finger found the next hole. The voice sounded oddly unlike her own. She met his gaze and caught at her lower lip with her teeth, hardly knowing whether to believe him or not. He was just about ruthless enough to be telling the truth. 'Supposing I got to the authorities first?' she said.

'You would not be allowed.' He waited a moment longer, then removed his finger from the dial and replaced the receiver. 'I regret the necessity for such tactics, but my need is too great for finer feeling to hold much sway. Tomorrow at sunset, Carlos will be married to Isabella. Before then I must return with a wife. Will you agree to do as I ask?'

She looked back at him helplessly. 'But my job—the Agency.'

'All will be taken care of. Do I have your word?'

'Will I be kept a prisoner if I give it?'

'No.' The dark eyes held hers. 'But should you break it there is no place in the city where I could not find you. And when I did . . .' He left it there. 'Your word.'

'You don't leave me any alternative.' She was shaken, and still not able to take it all in. 'All right, I give you my word.'

'Good.' Visibly he relaxed. 'Now we can finish our meal.'

'Why me?' she begged as he reached again for the basket of rolls. 'Why pick on me?'

'Because everything about you is perfect for the task. You have no family waiting for news of you, no unbreakable commitments; you are not bound by the conventions of my countrywomen, and you are in need of money.'

'Not this badly,' she retorted bitterly. 'I agreed because

you forced me into it, not for the money. I'm still not sure you weren't bluffing about Rios.'

'It matters little. You have given me your word on it.'

'And you trust me to keep it.'

The powerful shoulders lifted. 'I trust you to have the good sense to keep it. Should you fail me now you will wish to heaven you *were* back with Rios. Do I make myself understood?'

'Perfectly.' The warmth showed faint beneath her skin. 'I should be grateful ours is only a business arrangement.'

His smile held a taunt. 'Perhaps so. You would find the Latin too demanding a lover for your tastes.'

'What would *you* know of my tastes!'

Black brows rose. 'You think me wrong in my assessment? There is one way to be certain.'

She said hastily, 'You promised me a purely businesslike relationship.'

'So? There are other Latins who would be only too pleased to provide you with a comparison. Should you be of the same opinion when the time comes for the two of us to separate I could arrange the experience for you.'

'I didn't——' she began, then stopped abruptly. He knew she hadn't meant it that way without being told. She was just being got at. 'I'd choose my own lover if I wanted one,' she said instead.

'But not within the coming six months.' There was a warning in his tone. 'Business relationship or not, the wife of a Mendoza must conduct herself with the utmost circumspection. In the eyes of everyone else our marriage must appear real and valid. Any deviation on your part from the lines I lay down for your behaviour would be dealt with in the accustomed manner. You are going to earn your fee, every penny of it!'

'So I'm beginning to realise.' Lian forced herself to coolness, smothering the urge to tell him she wouldn't go through with it no matter what he threatened to do. If there was one

chance in a thousand of his placing her back in Rio's hands
she couldn't afford to take it. But she could, and would,
make things difficult for him. 'On the face of it,' she added,
'I don't think ten thousand is going to be enough. I want
twenty.'

The silence was weighty, the narrowing of his eyes a threat
in itself. With deliberation he allowed his gaze to move
slowly down from her face over the open neckline of her dress
to rest on the shapely curves below for a meaningful moment. 'I should make you pay dearly for that,' he said.

'And defeat your own purpose?' Her voice sounded thick
in her ears along with the thudding of her heartbeats. 'To
gain an annulment it's usually necessary to claim non-
consummation.'

'We are not yet married.'

'It would be your word against mine with regard to the
time and place. Dare you risk it for the sake of a few thousand
pounds?'

There were flecks of amber now in the darkness of his
eyes. From where she sat she could see the tensing of the
muscles along the line of his jaw.

'The money means little,' he said. 'But my offer was fair.
If you did as you intimate you would stand to lose all of it
and gain a husband who would take satisfaction in exacting
the utmost avengment. Dare *you* risk *that*?'

Her gaze fell, the breath catching in her throat. He had
her in a cleft stick, and he knew it. There was no getting the
better of a man like this. 'All right,' she said in low tones, 'so
I went too far.'

'Yes, you did.' The contempt seared. 'You may have
fifteen.'

Her head jerked up. 'No, I don't want it! I only—I
wanted——'

'You will take it.' He was angry still but in control of
himself. 'You are right—I should expect more than just a
fair price for such a service.'

'Señor Mendoza'—her tone was desperate—'please don't make me go through with this! I—can't!'

'You can and will, or you know the alternative.'

'I don't believe you about Rios!'

'It makes little difference now whether you believe me or not. You already gave me your word on the matter. I will not allow you to break it.' He stood up, pushing back the chair with a leashed violence more indicative of his closeness to practising it than any words. 'Tomorrow the marriage will take place, then we fly immediately to the *estancia*. In the meantime you will stay right here in the hotel unless I am with you.' For one long moment more he stood there apprais-ing the slender length of her, and something tautened about his mouth. 'Go on back to your own room,' he said. 'By the time we meet again we must both be in a better frame of mind.'

Lian left without argument, thankful to be free, even for a little while, of the sheer domination of him. Reaching her room, she leaned against the door and tried to rationalise her thoughts. It was all too fantastic, too unbelievable. Was it possible she was really dreaming the whole thing—or at least this part of it?

She knew it wasn't. The detail was too clear. No, it was really happening to her and she had to decide what she was going to do. Yet wasn't that decision already made? Ricardo Mendoza was not a man to make idle claims. If he said he could find her wherever she hid in the city, then he would find her. And then? A tremor ran through her. She didn't want to find out. Women here had little redress against male injustice, it appeared.

The morning passed slowly. Within the air-conditioned room, the outer heat was merely an impression, a shimmer along white roof edges, a hazing over of the sky. Lian studied the two glossy magazines left in the room, under-standing only a small amount of the Spanish but able to get the gist of one or two articles.

The ring of the telephone at midday was almost welcome. Ricardo sounded cool and clipped over the line.

'You would like luncheon in your room, or will you join me in the restaurant?' he inquired.

The decision came quickly. What was the use of staying away from him? If she was going to go through with this thing she had to start accustoming herself to his company. And she was going through with it. There was nothing surer. But not for the money, because she refused to allow herself to think about that part of it yet.

'I'll join you,' she said.

'Good.' Almost imperceptibly his tone had softened. 'I will meet you in fifteen minutes' time in the foyer.'

Fifteen minutes. Lian ran a mental eye over her wardrobe, still for the most part packed in her case. Not trousers, that was for certain. It didn't leave a lot of choice.

Eventually she decided on a white tricel pleated shirtwaister which needed no pressing, sliding her feet into matching sandals and fastening a black and white bandeau over her hair—not exactly the quality of outfit a rich man's wife would wear, but adequate to the present occasion. She wondered what Ricardo intended to do about clothes for her coming role. Not that so many would be needed on a ranch. Perhaps there she might even be allowed to wear her own jeans and slacks. In fact, she would insist on it. He might have her tied to this bargain they had struck, but she was not going to spend the six months as anyone but herself.

The foyer was busy with people both coming and going or just standing chatting in groups. Lian spotted one or two likely tourists, and wondered what would happen if she appealed to them for help. She even slowed near one elderly couple who looked as if they might be English, but the sight of Ricardo watching her from the restaurant doorway some short distance away hurried her footsteps past again.

Mouth sardonic, he said, 'You did well not to give way to impulse just now. I would have found little difficulty in convincing those two that my rebel of a young English wife was indulging her sense of humour at their expense.'

'I'm not your wife yet,' she responded, for want of any better retort, and saw him shrug.

'As of now you are playing the part. Tread carefully, *querida*. You have much to learn.'

The restaurant was full, but Ricardo, of course, had a table reserved. Seated at it in the semi-private alcove halfway down the room, Lian studied the huge menu and found the words dancing before her eyes. Eventually she put it down.

'You choose for me,' she said. 'I—I'm not very hungry.'

He gave her a swift glance, reeled off a variety of dishes to the waiting *camerero* and requested the presence of the wine waiter before returning his attention.

'You must eat,' he said. 'You had nothing but coffee at breakfast.'

Her smile was faint. 'That's hardly surprising. You should have provided brandy.'

Just for a moment his lip twitched in response. 'You think I am an ogre?'

'I think you're ruthless,' she said. 'You don't care about anyone or anything but this ranch of yours.'

'*Estancia*,' he corrected. 'You must begin calling things by the correct term. How much Spanish do you understand?'

'Not a lot, unless it's spoken very slowly. I can speak about the same amount, though my pronunciation isn't quite all it should be.'

'So I noted last night. By the time you leave the country you should be proficient in the language, if in nothing else.'

She said blandly, 'You've given up the idea of teaching me the Argentinian way to be a woman?'

'Not entirely. But six months will barely be long enough for all you will need to learn, and I would prefer that our relationship was as trouble-free as possible.' He held her gaze. 'This morning you angered me to the point of forgetting your nationality and basic nature. So we effect a compromise. If you will indulge me in public I will endeavour to turn a blind eye to your failings when we are alone together. Agreed?'

'Agreed.' The alone together bit brought a momentary return of doubt, but she squashed it. Not for anything would he jeopardise his plans for future freedom, certainly not for the sake of possessing a female he felt nothing for. She wondered if he had ever known love for a woman. It was doubtful. His contempt was for the sex, not just the individual. No, a man like him would use them when he found it desirous, but keep his mind and his heart intact. He probably wasn't capable of love; some people weren't.

'Hadn't you better tell me something about the *estancia*?' she suggested. 'Who lives there apart from you and your brother?'

'My half-brother,' he corrected on a hard note. 'And not even that with any right.'

'I'm sorry.' She waited a moment before saying softly, 'You really do hate him, don't you?'

'I have good reason. Not that you will agree when you meet him.' The firm mouth twisted. 'Carlos can charm the birds down from the trees when he sets his mind to it. Only with me does he become what he really is.'

'What is he?'

'The word is not for your ears.'

'I didn't mean it literally. I meant——' she paused, searching for the words, aware of the drawing together of his brows and knowing she was treading on delicate ground—'is it simply because he *is* illegitimate that you despise him, or because he's popular with everybody else?'

'While I am not,' he tagged on for her with irony.

'That isn't what I said.'

'It is what you implied. And in that you are right. I make few friends—though those I have I keep.' The arrival of the wine waiter forestalled any further comment for the moment. He gave the order, sitting back as the man departed to eye her shrewdly across the table between them. 'What I know of Carlos is not your affair. For five years now, since my father first became ill, I have run the *estancia* as it should be run. I do not intend to relinquish that control.'

'But Carlos will continue to live there?'

'Until another house can be built for him and Isabella they may both stay. Unless he chooses to run the Riga Estancia instead. Isabella's father grows old. He would welcome his son-in-law's help. Eventually it will be his, in any case.'

'Isabella is an only child?'

'Yes. With her mother and mine it was the same. They almost lost their lives giving birth and could have no more.'

Which could explain Carlos, Lian reflected. Aloud she said, 'Is the Riga Estancia cattle too?'

'Not wholly.' His lip had curled. 'Francisco also runs sheep.'

'Is that bad?'

'For the cattle it is not good. Sheep close-crop the alfalfa and kill it off. No true cattleman would have them on his land.' He shook his head impatiently. 'We deviate from the point. You asked about others. At the house there is only Inez, who was once my nurse and is now in charge of the servants. Sixty kilometres away lies the township of Santina. You will not go there unless I am with you.'

Lian lifted her head. 'Then I'm to be confined to the *estancia*?'

His smile was not unpleasant. 'You may not find it quite so restricting as you imagine. It takes a day to ride to one boundary. You have ridden a horse before?'

'Not often, and not with any expertise.'

'Then you will have another accomplishment to take back to England with you. I shall teach you myself.'

'I can't wait,' she said dryly, and saw the glint spring in the dark eyes.

'Nor I. You recover quickly from chastisement.'

'Have I been chastised?'

His regard was almost indulgent. 'Short of beating you I see no way of creating a lasting impression, However, time will tell. Our food is coming. You will please me by trying a little of everything. After we. have eaten we will look at the sights of the city for your benefit. Tomorrow there may not be time.'

Tomorrow. Lian felt her throat go dry. Tomorrow she was to marry this man; this stranger—this abductor ! It didn't bear thinking about, yet there was no way out—at least not one she dared take. It was all the Agency's fault. She would think about sueing them when she got back. *If* she got back. Six months seemed a lifetime. Anything could happen.

CHAPTER THREE

FROM three thousand feet the horizons seemed limitless, the plains below flat and vast, with only the occasional criss-crossing lines of the endless dirt roads to break the monotony. 'When you see the skyline to the south begin rising to a range of low hills then we are almost there,' Ricardo had said some time back. 'The Sierra de Tandil borders Mendoza land.' So far there was no sign of a change in the spreading blue-tinted grassland, although the distances to the south were hazed with heat.

Lian glanced sideways at the man she had married bare hours ago; at the lean brown capability of his hands on the controls. It was difficult to believe that so much could have happened in just two days, yet here she was—the Señora Mendoza, wife of one of the richest men in the Argentine, and totally out of her depth. This world of private planes and untold wealth wasn't and never could be hers. She wouldn't want it to be hers. Enduring six months of it was going to take all she had.

The ceremony had been performed with the minimum of fuss in an atmosphere of cold officialdom that had left her untouched by any kind of feeling. Realisation had come later, on the way to the airfield out by the river used by domestic traffic. The man at her side was now her husband, with the authority over her of a culture in which women were still very much secondary citizens. The thought was daunting.

A little desperately, she turned her mind back to the previous night, trying to recapture the spirit of adventure which had carried her through. Ricardo had taken her out to one of the city's most sumptuous nightspots, after first buying her the kind of dress every woman dreams of. Wearing it had changed her, given her confidence in herself. She knew other men had looked at her with approval, and at Ricardo with envy, and she had loved every moment of it. Vanity, she thought now. There was more to life than that. She wished she were a million miles from here, from this whole situation. She wanted to go home.

Ricardo looked her way for a moment, eyes assessing. 'You are very quiet,' he said. 'Are you suddenly afraid of me?'

'I don't know you.' Her voice was low and ragged. 'I don't know you at all, and I don't understand you.'

'Understanding will come, if you want it to. Not that it will matter too much should it not.'

'Providing I just do as I'm told.'

He smiled and shrugged. 'That is one way of putting it. I prefer to say as you are asked.'

'You didn't do a great deal of asking yesterday.'

'Yesterday was different. I was forced to bully you into agreeing with what I wanted from you. There was no time for gentler persuasion.'

She was silent for quite a length of time. 'You mean,' she said at last, 'that you *were* bluffing when you threatened to take me back to the Club Rios?'

'Yes. He would not have wanted you back unless you were willing. Rios is a man of small honour, but he is no fool.'

'You tricked me.' Her face was pale and taut. 'You set up the whole thing!'

'I told you, my need was desperate. I had doubts myself when we reached the hotel, but I overcame them. You must do the same.' There was irony in his voice. 'Surely it is better to know I am not quite so ruthless as you first imagined?'

Lian couldn't see what difference it made. She was here, wasn't she? He had taken advantage of her gullibility, and that was ruthless enough.

'I would prefer us to be friends,' he said, 'rather than enemies. It would make matters easier.'

'For you or for me?'

'For both of us. You are used to earning your living. Can you not regard this as just another job? It is only for six months.'

She said with intent, 'Supposing I refuse to go after six months? Have you thought about that?'

Something altered in his face, turning it taut and alien again. 'You would not dare,' he stated with flat intonation.

He was right about that, she acknowledged ruefully. She wouldn't dare. Nor would she want to. Six months would be more than enough.

'You don't have to worry,' she said. 'I won't make any difficulties. I'll be glad to be free of you.'

'I will make sure of it.' He indicated ahead through the screen. 'We are almost there. In a moment or two you will see the airstrip.'

The day was well advanced, the light turning opaque. The line of hills set against the far horizon seemed to waver and ripple like water. Perhaps a mile further on from their immediate descent, Lian could make out the darker lines of a group of buildings surrounded by trees. Closer, cattle grazed in a large herd watched over by men on horseback, moving slowly over the oddly bluish-tinted grassland. There was nothing else in sight but the occasional upthrust of a windpump, the outline of a water tank.

'The herd is being gathered for the drive across to the railhead,' Ricardo informed her, sensing the unspoken question. 'From there they go directly to La Plata on the coast where the *frigoríficos* are situated.'

To be killed and cut up and frozen for the world's tables, Lian reflected. Aloud she said, 'They don't have much of a life, do they?'

His shrug was indifferent. 'Only the English are sentimental about such matters. The animals are bred for beef.'

Touchdown was smooth, the Cessna rolling to a stop within yards of the small group of buildings at one end of the marked cross-strip. The man who came out of one of them was roughly clad and of mixed blood, his features dark and coarse, his manner servile. Lian smiled at him, and was rewarded by a blank stare in return. Ricardo spoke to him shortly in Spanish, then led Lian across to a waiting estate car while the other fetched their luggage from the plane. He set off immediately it was stored away in the rear compartment without speaking to the man again.

'Is *he* bred to serve?' Lian asked with irony as they took to the dirt road, and he glanced at her with a quick frown.

'Is that meant to be humorous?'

'No,' she said. 'I don't find it in the least bit funny to see human beings treated like cattle. Didn't the man have a name?'

His nostrils pinched. 'I do not introduce my wife to a *péon*! The ways of our country are not as yours.'

'You're right,' she said, 'they're not. In my country serfdom went out with the Middle Ages.'

'These people are not enslaved. They are free to come and go as and when they please.'

'How? Judging from the clothes he was wearing they don't have much in the way of material assets. What do you pay them?'

'That is enough,' he said coldly. 'It is not your affair.'

'It has to be my affair if I'm to act the part of your wife. Or are women supposed to turn a blind eye to the needs of the lower classes?'

'You will be quiet!' He hadn't raised his voice, but the tone was emphatic. 'I will not be catechised this way by any female. Do you wish to feel the weight of my hand?'

Lian sighed. 'Is that your answer to everything?'

'No, not everything. Just to an English girl who imagines herself inviolate from such treatment.' He glanced her way when she failed to come up with any retort, mouth purposefully set. 'I told you conformation with our ways was a necessary part of our bargain. I have no particular desire to be forced to put you in your place before others.'

The sun was setting behind a bank of cloud building from the distant western rim, the reddened glow lighting the featureless landscape. She was far from home in another world, and entirely alone. She swallowed on the sudden hard lump in her throat, said huskily, 'Ricardo, I have to be myself—don't you see that? I can't act the way an Argentinian woman would. I might ask questions which anger you; I might not be satisfied with the answers, but that's the way I am. If I try not to do it in front of others will *you* try to treat me as an equal when we're alone, as you said you would?'

One brow had lifted. 'I do not remember ever promising to treat you as an equal.'

'The phrase you used was "indulge my failings", I think. Well, those *are* my failings. You aren't going to cure them with threats and admonitions, but you might quiet them by taking me into your confidence. I'd like to learn something about your country while I'm here. You could teach me. I won't promise to like all of it, though.'

There was a long pause before he began to smile. 'I know no other woman who speaks to a man the way you do,' he said. 'Perhaps I too have something to learn. Very well, I will do my best to curb my impulses where you are concerned, though I cannot promise never to become angry with you. Does that make you any happier?'

'Yes, quite a lot.' She looked ahead at the darkening plain, seeing lights far in the distance. 'Is that the house?'

'The *casa* is in the other direction,' he returned on a suddenly hardened note. 'We are going now to the wedding feast.'

'Oh no!' Lian sat up straight, her eyes flying to his face. 'Ricardo, you can't!'

'I must.' The statement was implacable. 'It will do no good

to try to change my mind. Carlos must know at the earliest possible moment that he does not own the Estancia Mendoza.'

'But it will ruin the wedding!'

'He will get over it.'

'And Isabella?' She searched the lean features for some sign of softening. 'Do you hate her too?'

'No.' He gripped the wheel more firmly, lips compressed. 'But in marrying Carlos she loses the right to my consideration.'

'At least wait till morning,' she begged. 'Let them have tonight. Please, Ricardo!'

'You think it kinder to allow them to return to Mendoza and find us there?'

'I don't know. Yes! Yes, it has to be. Anything is better than breaking in on the wedding itself!'

'I do not agree.' There was no sign of relenting. 'The sooner it is over the better.'

Lian said nothing more. It was obviously going to be useless. With heavy heart she watched the lights come closer, saw the buildings themselves take on shape. The house was a low, two-storied building set around a central courtyard, the latter approached through a white stone archway. Music came from within, the sound of guitars and fiddles mingling with the shouts and laughter of the crowd spilling out through the archway on to the forecourt. Some of the latter turned as Ricardo drove in past the perimeter fencing and brought the car to a stop, faces registering differing reactions in the flickering light from torches and lanterns.

A *péon* detached himself from the edge of the group and came over quickly to open the door of the car, murmuring a respectful greeting in his own language. He was wearing spotless white cotton trousers and shirt, with a gay neckerchief at his throat, and held a soft, wide-brimmed hat across his chest. He wasn't very old, Lian saw. Perhaps twenty three or four. She felt the dark eyes fasten on her as she got out of the car, heard the swift little buzz of comment which ran through the watchers. She smiled and tried to look at ease as Ricardo led her towards the archway, feeling anything but as those in front fell back to allow them free passage.

The courtyard within was all light and colour, the walls arched and balconied and festooned with flowers. There were tables down the centre of it laden with food, and a milling crowd of guests, many of them wearing traditional Spanish costume.

The bride and groom stood together on a raised patio at the far end of the courtyard, along with an elderly couple Lian took to be the parents of the bride. She felt Ricardo's arm stiffen a little under hers as his eyes sought the dark flashing beauty of the girl in the long ornate white dress, and knew with sudden distressing certainty that her husband had more than one reason for hating his half-brother. He had wanted Isabella for himself.

Someone recognised Ricardo close by, and set up a shout equivalent to 'Look who's here!' Once again Lian recognised a mixed reaction; some uncertain, some dismayed; and one or two obviously delighted—all of them immediately curious about her presence. Ricardo nodded acknowledgement right and left, but made no attempt to speak to anyone, leading her down the opening passageway to where the bridal party stood waiting in attitudes of frozen expectancy.

Carlos was of a shorter, stockier building than his half-brother, his face handsomely bold, hair black and curling. He was dressed in an outfit which reminded Lian of a matador's, the trousers tight and fitted to the legs in a cloth of black and gold thread, the short jacket hugging his broad chest over a white silk shirt with full sleeves. He looked magnificent, and was aware of it.

'So, my brother,' he said in Spanish, 'you come back for my wedding! And you bring a guest!' The smile he turned on Lian was dazzling in its refusal to acknowledge the possibilities implicit in her presence. 'Welcome, *señorita*.'

'*Señora*,' corrected Ricardo without particular inflection.

'We were married this morning in Buenos Aires.'

In the sudden stillness, Lian found her eyes drawn to the lovely face of the bride, and for a fleeting moment was sure she saw relief there. She had to be mistaken, of course. Why should any woman be glad that her husband had lost everything? She hated herself for what she was doing; hated Ricardo for being the instrument of her participation. No matter what the rights and wrongs of the situation, this was no way to solve it.

Carlos was the first to speak, his voice low and quivering with suppressed emotion. 'That is impossible!'

'I have the proof, if you wish to see it.' There was no note of triumph in Ricardo's tone, just a statement of fact. His eyes on Isabella, he slid a deliberate arm about Lian's shoulders and drew her closer to his side. 'My wife is English, and speaks little Spanish, unfortunately. But she will learn.'

Isabella stirred, dark eyes veiled as she stepped forward and put out both her hands in greeting. 'Welcome, my sister,' she said quietly in English. 'You must share in our wedding feast, you and Ricardo.'

Francisco Riga moved towards his son-in-law. 'Carlos, this changes things,' Lian understood him to say. 'Our home is now yours.' A hand laid on the younger man's arm stayed the refutal trembling on his lips. 'It is for the best, my son.'

Lian had moved from within Ricardo's grasp to return Isabella's hand clasp, her limbs heavy as her heart. It was too late to say how sorry she was for what was happening, but she tried to convey with her eyes what she felt, perceiving a faint glimmer of understanding in the dark ones. A murmur of admiration travelled through the assembled company at the contrast made between dark and light heads so close together. '*Noches y días,*' someone whispered.

Ricardo looked on with a faint smile on his lips which did not touch his eyes.

'We will not stay,' he said. 'The journey has been tiring. Lian will wish to rest.'

'But it is your wedding day,' Isabella protested. 'Yours *and* ours. You cannot leave yet, Ricardo. Not until the toasts have been made. Would you deny your bride the right to future happiness?' She turned before he could speak, reaching for her husband's hand and bringing him forward to her side. 'Carlos, you agree they must stay a little while longer? We are all of one family now.'

The younger man's eyes were hot and passionate as they rested on the face of his brother, but his nod of assent was controlled. 'Of course. There is no reason now to hurry. Come, it is time to eat. You will share a place with Isabella and myself.'

Ricardo's shrug was indifferent. Hating him as she had never hated anyone before, Lian allowed him to lead her alongside Isabella and Carlos to the topmost table, to seat her next to the other girl and take his own seat on her left with Carlos on the far side completing the quartet. Conscious of the eyes upon them, and of the creased state of her own cream linen suit against the beautifully embroidered dress of her neighbour, she held her head high and tried to look at ease, knowing she failed miserably.

'You have known Ricardo for long?' asked Isabella as the servers began bringing round the platters of food.

For long? She didn't, Lian realised, even know how long he had been in Buenos Aires this trip! He was listening for her reply, face registering no concern for what it might be. Very well then, so they could have the truth. He deserved no better than that.

'Two days,' she said without looking at him, and heard the other girl's faint gasp.

'That—is a very short time,' she said after a moment. 'You must have known your heart at once when you met.'

'Oh yes.' And she should have listened to it, Lian thought bitterly. Aloud she added, with deliberation. 'Being rescued from a fate worse than death places one under great obligation.'

Isabella's eyes had widened. 'I do not think——' she began doubtfully.

'One thing you will come to learn about my wife, Isabella,' Ricardo put in on a measured note, 'is that her sense of the humorous is not quite as ours. Lian means simply to joke with you.' The slight but distinct pressure of his knee against hers beneath the table was a threat in itself. 'Is that not right, *chica*?'

'If you say so.' Her heart was hammering, but something stronger than trepidation had her in its grip. 'You are always right, Ricardo.'

If those close enough to hear understood the words themselves it was doubtful that they caught the inflection, but it was not wasted on the man at her side. She heard the slight hiss of his indrawn breath, and turned back at once to meet Isabella's somewhat uncertain regard with a bright smile. 'Ricardo says I must cultivate the Argentinian manner in my attitude towards him. Perhaps you would help me to learn the right ways?'

The other's expression lightened, a smile breaking out. 'Ah, now you tease me again, I think!'

'Yes.' Lian was suddenly ashamed of what she was doing. It wasn't fair to draw Isabella into this in any way. The matter was between her and Ricardo. Stifling the involuntary little quiver that acknowledgment brought, she said softly, 'Forgive me, Isabella, I am behaving badly.'

'No,' with a laugh. 'You behave differently, but it is a difference I find diverting. Do you not find it so too, Carlos?'

The handsome swarthy face had an odd expression. 'It is —interesting,' he agreed. He looked directly across her to Ricardo. 'Your wife is one with spirit—and daring. You have been fortunate in finding her.'

'You are right, Lian is extremely daring.' The tolerance in Ricardo's voice was not designed to deceive. 'We have both of us been fortunate in our choice, eh, Carlos? Isabella makes a radiant bride.'

Lian looked around the brilliant colourful scene, listened to the many voices speaking the language she was only just beginning to learn in any depth and wondered what on earth she was doing here. It didn't feel real, any of it. Ricardo was her husband, yet she didn't love him; didn't even like him. He was not only ruthless, he was cruel into the bargain. There had been no need for this confrontation, at least not at such a time. He had done it as much to punish Isabella as Carlos. But Carlos hadn't stolen her from him, he had simply taken what was rightfully his. Isabella loved him; it was there in the way she looked at him, the way she spoke. Could Ricardo not see the unfairness of punishing a woman for preferring someone else?

If he could he did not make it evident. During the following hour of feasting he continued to sit there as though in judgment, speaking when spoken to but otherwise contributing little to the occasion. Lian hardly knew whether to be glad or sorry when he announced a disinclination to stay for the dancing and revelry which would go on into the early hours.

'We had a long journey,' he said, 'and still have to reach home.' His eyes met those of his half-brother. 'It is still your home too, should you wish it. Yours and Isabella's.'

'No, we stay here. This is our home now.' Carlos spoke with a coolness belied by the glitter in his gaze. 'You have won Mendoza, Ricardo. I want no part of it.' There was ambiguity in the latter statement.

They were in the car and driving away from the *casa* into the starlit darkness of the plain before Lian could bring herself to speak.

'That was one of the worst experiences of my life,' she said.

'And of mine,' he agreed.

Her head whipped round towards him, but there was nothing to be gleaned from the enigmatic expression. 'Then why did you do it?' she asked.

'I have told you why—because it was necessary to get it over with. This way Carlos had to accept. No man desires to make trouble on his wedding day.'

Apart from himself, Lian thought with irony, although there was a difference in the circumstances, she supposed.

'I thought Carlos acted commendably well,' she said. 'No matter how ill-founded his entitlement to the Estancia Mendoza might be, few men could have taken the loss of it the way he did.'

'You admire him for that?' His voice was silky smooth.

'Yes, I do,' on a note of defiance. 'Shouldn't I?'

It was a moment or two before he answered, features hard and austere in the semi-darkness. 'You must please yourself how you feel about Carlos inside. All I demand is that you appear loyal to me on the surface.'

'That goes without question.'

'It does?' The smile was grim. 'We shall see. Six months is a long time.'

And getting longer by the minute, Lian acknowledged heavily. She looked out of the window at the dark expanse of plain. 'I'm going to hate it here,' she said half to herself.

'How can you hate what you know so little about?' he demanded sharply. 'A child may make instant judgments; from you I expect a balanced one. You said you wished to learn about my country.'

'I know, and I do. It's just'— she paused before finishing it—'the situation. I might have made a friend of Isabella if things had been different.'

'Had things been different you would not be here at all,' he pointed out with undisputable logic. 'And because of the circumstances I would prefer that your association with anyone outside of my own household remains distant. Should Carlos begin to suspect the truth he would lose little time in taking advantage of it.'

'How? By offering me more money to leave before the six

months are up?' Lian shook her head, voice purposely light. 'I doubt if he could afford it now.'

Ricardo brought the car to a halt with a jerk, the expression on his face disquietening.

'The money I offered you in return for your services is all my own,' he said between his teeth. 'My mother was a wealthy woman in her own right. She left everything in trust for me until I reached the age of twenty-five. The Estancia Mendoza means more to me than its value in financial terms. Not that I would expect you to understand that, any more than Carlos does. As to his own financial status—he will continue to receive an income from Mendoza for as long as he lives.'

'If he takes it,' she murmured defensively.

'He will take it. There is nothing more certain.' Eyes glittering, he added, 'Your concern for Carlos is touching on such short acquaintance. Do you envy Isabella the attentions of such a man tonight?'

Her face flamed in the darkness. 'Don't be ridiculous!' she snapped back, and gave a small cry of pain as his hand flashed out to seize her roughly under the chin and jerk up her head.

'You will not call me that,' he said with deadly quietness. 'You were immediately attracted to Carlos; I saw it in your eyes. A pity that such an emotion should have to go unsatisfied.'

Lian struggled as he drew her towards him in the same inexorable grip, but she was helpless to break it. His mouth was ruthless, the anger in him searing. Almost unable to breathe, she suffered the hardness of his hands on her, the total lack of tenderness in his embrace. When he finally pushed her away from him back into her seat she felt drained of all emotion, even hatred. She couldn't bring herself to look at him as he put the car into sudden violent motion again.

She was still in no fit state to take in much about the Mendoza *casa* when they eventually arrived, except that it seemed much larger than the one they had left some twenty minutes before. There were trees around it, and many outbuildings beyond. Lights burned inside.

Ricardo made no attempt to speak as he assisted her from the car. Face totally expressionless, he led her to double, dark wood doors which opened directly into a magnificent terrazzo-floored hall. The furnishings were huge and dark and heavy with carving, the fireplace stretching from floor to ceiling in the same light-coloured stone as the outer walls of the house. Silver glinted from practically every surface, the pieces intricately worked and beautiful. Lian gazed in fascination at a solid representation of the Four Horsemen of the Apocalypse standing in front of the empty iron fire casket in the grate. That alone must be worth a fortune.

An elderly woman descended the curving wrought iron staircase set against the side wall, her plain black dress high cut and severe, her lined features inscrutable. Only on looking at Ricardo did she allow the mask to slip a little, her eyes softening in fondness.

'Welcome back, *señor*,' she said formally. 'It is good to know you are home again.'

'I am glad to be back,' he acknowledged. His hand was still beneath Lian's elbow, his touch impersonal now. 'This is Inez,' he added in English with cool inflection. 'She has been with the Mendoza family for more than forty years.' He broke back at once into Spanish. 'My wife, Inez. She speaks our language but little as yet.'

Had the housekeeper already been advised of her master's marriage she could not have revealed less surprise. Her acknowledgment was stiff and unsmiling. '*Señora*.'

'We shall be using the west rooms,' Ricardo continued. 'How long will it take to prepare them?'

'Only a short time. I will see to it myself.'

He turned back to Lian as the Spanish woman ascended the stairs again. 'You would like a drink while we wait?'

She hesitated, uncertain of his present mood and unwilling to do or say anything which might spark off a repetition of angry scorn. 'I'd like some coffee, please,' she said at last in the same language, and saw him push a hand over his hair in a sudden weary gesture.

'I am sorry. Spanish comes more readily to me now I am home.'

'I don't mind,' she was quick to assure him. 'It will be good for me. I can understand a great deal providing it's said reasonably slowly.'

His expression lost none of its coolness. 'That could be more trouble than speaking English. Come.' He took her arm again.

More double doors beneath the curve of the staircase led through into another huge room. In here the floors were covered in thickly piled carpet the colour of cream. Massive hide sofas formed a three-sided square in front of a fireplace even bigger than the one outside, draped with rugs in subtly worked colours. There were several low tables scattered around, some inlaid with silver, some in a variety of woods. Wide glass doors gave on to a covered terrace, with arches leading out to the central courtyard.

'All the rooms downstairs give on to the courtyard,' Ricardo said, following the line of her gaze as he pressed a bell push. 'Several of the bedrooms overlook it. It is customary to dine out there when entertaining guests. It is, as you might say, the focal point of the home.'

He gave an order to the young girl dressed simply in cotton skirt and blouse who had appeared in answer to his summons, then took a seat on the sofa opposite to the one Lian had chosen and got out a cheroot. She waited until he had lit it and drawn on it a couple of times before saying quietly:

'You have a beautiful home, Ricardo.'

He inclined his head. 'It has changed little since my mother died. Her tastes were for the simpler lines. Only the outer hall remains typically Spanish.'

Lian found her eyes drawn to the portrait hanging above the fireplace, depicting a young woman of the same kind of dark flashing beauty she had seen in Isabella, her scarlet, multi-flounced dress cut low to leave the creamy shoulders bare. 'Is that your mother?' she asked.

'Yes. It was done shortly after her marriage.'

'She was very lovely.'

'Yes,' he said again. Voice totally dispassionate, he added, 'She was only forty years of age when she died, but you would not have recognised her.'

Why? Lian wanted to ask, but daren't. 'How old were you?' she said instead.

'Nineteen.' His lips twisted. 'Old enough to know what the knowledge of duplicity can do to the heart and mind. The Mendoza Estancia was barely a third of the size it is today before it became joined with that of my mother's family.'

Was he saying that his father had married his mother only for that purpose? Lian wondered. It would explain so much; especially his determination not to allow Carlos control of the land which was his by right of descent on both sides.

'Are none of your mother's relatives still living?' she queried.

'Two sisters—my aunts. One of them lives in Buenos Aires.'

And both on incomes drawn from Mendoza; he didn't have to say it, Lian knew it.

The arrival of the coffee created a welcome diversion just at that moment. Lian returned Juanita's shy smile as she took the cup from her, glad of a friendly face. The coffee was both bitter and stronger than she preferred it, but it felt good. She drank half of it for courage before putting down the cup and saucer on the nearest table and looking across at Ricardo.

'I'd like to say I'm sorry for what I said earlier,' she offered tentatively. 'I didn't understand all the circumstances.'

'And you believe you do now?' on a note of irony.

'Better than I did, anyway. If you'd told me that much before——'

'I have told you as much only because it seemed necessary to gain some loyalty to our bargain from you.' He paused, mouth taking on a harder slant. 'And do not expect an apology from me for what happened between us. You deserved no better. Not that you need concern yourself it will happen again. Next time you provoke me to violence I will find some other means of venting my feelings.'

Her face felt set. 'There won't be a next time.'

'I trust not.'

Inez appeared in the doorway behind him. 'The rooms are ready,' she said.

'Good.' His eyes found Lian's again, cool and incalculable. 'Inez will show you where you will sleep when you have finished your coffee.'

Lian took up the cup and drained it without regard to the heat on her lips. 'I have finished,' she said. 'I'm ready now.'

She stood up, aware of the older woman's presence and oddly embarrassed by the situation. 'Goodnight, then.'

'*Buenas noches*,' he said with satire.

The room seemed over-large as she crossed it, knowing his eyes followed her. Inez turned without a word and led the way to the staircase, her back ramrod straight as she climbed. An open gallery ran the width of the rear wall, with a windowless corridor cutting in from the centre. Inez stopped at the second door down on the left, pushing it open and standing back with the same expressionless face to allow Lian to precede her.

Predictably the room was large, the furnishing luxurious and surprisingly modern in appearance. There was a fireplace in here too, Lian realised they would all be needed in the Argentinian winters when the temperatures dropped. Frost was not uncommon in some months, she believed.

Inez had followed her in. Now she walked across the room to open another door. '*De bano*,' she said.

Her own bathroom. She smiled. '*Gracias*, Inez.'

The woman did not return the smile, acknowledging the words with a faint movement of her head, and going back to the outer door. '*Buenas noches, señora*,' she said.

Alone at last, Lian gazed for a moment at the nightdress lying ready across the turned-down bed. Inez, or somebody, must have unpacked for her in the brief time they had had. Her suitcase was missing, spirited away, no doubt to some store room. She would not be seeing it again for six months.

Chest tight, she went over and opened the doors leading out on to the balcony, smelling the scent of the flowering vine climbing up the balustrade. Leaning over a little, she could see the light from the *salón* spilling out through the archway below over the paved courtyard. An ornamental well stood towards the rear, covered in flowers. More plants hung in baskets and grew in urns. The sound of the cicadas filled the air.

It was like an oasis, she thought: an island in the endless sea of grass out there beyond the walls. Perhaps she would grow accustomed to this land of Ricardo's, but she would never learn to love it. But then she didn't have to, did she? Any more than she had to learn to love him. This marriage wasn't real; she must keep telling herself that. It wasn't real.

CHAPTER FOUR

It took Lian a week to stop being depressed by the flat horizons that bound the views to three sides of Mendoza land, and gain compensation from the serrated line of hills forming the Sierra de Tandil in the south. The grassland might stretch unbroken but for the occasional clumps of bushes and low trees which acted as windbreaks, but up there were rocks of granite much like those of her home county back in England. It was the only area of familiarity she had to cling to.

The *casa* itself was built solely of that granite, brought down from the Sierras fifty years before by Ricardo's grandfather, the original house being added to over the years between until it had become the showplace it was today. Lian admired its magnificence, yet found it incongruous in such a setting, so far from the kind of society it was designed to impress. With the nearest town almost forty miles away, and no neighbours closer than the Rigas, there seemed little point in its size, for one thing. It took an enormous staff just to keep the place clean.

'There was a time when Mendoza was rarely without at least a half dozen guests,' Ricardo advised when she mentioned the subject casually to him one morning. 'I remember sitting as a child on the stairs peering through the balustrade at the people in their fine dress, hearing the music of the *fiesta*. There were many such occasions before Madre became ill.'

'Was she ill for long?' Lian queried with what she hoped was the right amount of semi-personal interest, and saw his face darken a shade.

'Too long,' he said. 'How are you coming along in your riding?'

She accepted the change of subject without visible reaction. 'Not too badly. José makes me ride without holding the reins so that I learn balance.' She smiled a little. 'It's odd that your foreman speaks absolutely no English yet finds no difficulty in putting across his meaning. I'm never in the least doubt as to his commands.'

The smile was returned, albeit with reserve. 'José's job is to command.'

'Under you.'

'Under me *and* my departmental managers, yes.' He studied her standing there in the sunlight of the courtyard in her blue jeans and gingham shirt. 'You should have more suitable clothing. Should you ride for any distance in those you have on your legs would become chafed where the leather rubs.'

'José loaned me a sheepskin to put over the saddle the way they do. It's very comfortable.'

'Sheepskins are for the *gauchos*,' he said with harsh inflection. 'You will discard it. If you tell me your size I will have some breeches and boots obtained for you in Santina.'

He was wearing beautifully cut riding breeches himself, the lower half of his legs encased in brown leather polished to a high shine. His shirt was open at the throat, with a kerchief knotted casually. The sun glinted on the black hair, uncovered at present though normally hidden beneath one of the soft-brimmed hats when he was on horseback.

'Are you going out?' she asked diffidently.

He nodded. 'I go to see how the branding comes along. The herd must be ready for shipment by the end of the week.'

'Is it far?'

'A matter of two of your miles perhaps to the railhead.' He paused. 'You would like to accompany me?'

'Oh yes!' Lian would have gone anywhere just for the change, even if it did mean spending time with Ricardo. He

was the only one with whom she could speak more than a
few words of English, and her Spanish, though improving,
still left a lot to be desired.

Life had settled into something of a pattern this last week.
They met for meals, and occasionally like this during the day,
but for the most part Ricardo seemed to go out of his way to
avoid being with her for too long a stretch of time. She
couldn't blame him. She was a constant reminder of the
lengths to which he had been forced to stoop in order to keep
Mendoza. This offer now was a concession she could not
afford to turn down.

Ricardo had provided her with a brimmed hat not unlike
his own which he had mentioned casually as once belonging
to his mother. The crown was hard-padded for protection,
she had found—apparently only women were expected to
fall off horses in these parts. They went out together to the
stables some small distance from the *casa*. While her mount
was being saddled for her, Lian took time off to study once
more the long, low lines of the house with its fretted iron
window grilles, the smooth sweep of close-cropped grass
fronting it down to the entrance archway, the green beauty
of the shade trees surrounding it. Hard to believe that this
was her home, even if only for a limited period. She still felt
as if she were living in a luxury hotel, with service second to
none.

A house like Mendoza needed children to create a more
homely atmosphere, she thought, and knew a faint tightening of her chest muscles. There would be no children because
Ricardo wanted no permanent marriage. When she was gone
he would live alone but for the servants. Inez would look
after him, of course, but she was old, and not given to much
conversation. To whom would he turn for stimulation of the
kind a man of his intelligence and knowledge would need
through the years? Whatever their own differences, at least
she provided him with some mental stimulus, judging from

the range of topics they had discussed during their brief times together.

The mare on which she had been learning was led out to join the great black stallion Ricardo always rode, the latter moving sharply in his holder's grip as he scented her, head jerking at the rein.

Ricardo said a few sharp words to the boy who had brought the newcomer, then demanded a substitute in no uncertain terms.

'The mare is coming into heat,' he said in disgust, as the animal was led away again. 'Do they not think this beast of mine difficult enough to handle!'

'Why do you ride him at all if he's so difficult to control?' Lian asked, masking her trepidation as to which of the other horses she was going to be expected to ride. 'He's magnificent, of course, but——'

'But dangerous,' he finished for her. His smile was faint. 'Perhaps that is the very reason I do ride him. He occupies my mind in addition to my hands.'

'You mean he has to be mastered.'

He shook his head. 'No man will ever master Diablo. We have an understanding, that is all, but the greatest rapport between man and beast cannot overrule the inclinations of nature. You would not have been happy, I think, had he attempted to mount your mare while you were still in the saddle.' He caught her startled upward glance and tilted his lips a little further this time. 'It would not have been the first time such a thing has happened. An animal has no fitting sense of time or place. Your life could have been in grave danger.'

To say nothing of her dignity. Lian forced a laugh. 'You'd have saved me, I'm sure,' she said, and saw his brow lift.

'Such trust?'

The tone stung enough to make her reckless. 'Well, you need me alive, don't you, to fulfil the terms of your father's will.'

Lips compressed, he said, 'Not necessarily. The only way it can be broken is by your knowing departure inside the stated time. And you will not be leaving, of that I can assure you. Come, your mount is ready.'

Lian followed him over to where the two horses stood waiting, mouth wry. She had asked for that, and Ricardo was not the man to let her get away with it. Dead, she would be here not just for six months, but for ever. She had already seen the family graveyard about a mile from the *casa*.

This time she had a gelding, a lean, rangy animal which rolled its eyes at her as Ricardo helped her into the saddle. From the way Diablo still seemed to be reacting she only hoped he could tell the difference. She gathered the reins nervously.

'Not so tightly,' Ricardo admonished. 'Do you wish to communicate to the beast that you are afraid of it?'

'I'm not afraid,' she denied. 'Just naturally cautious. This is the first time I've ridden anything but the mare.'

'Then it is more than time you had a change. José should not have allowed it.'

She looked down at the dark head as he adjusted one of her stirrups. 'You ride only Diablo.'

'The difference being that I am not a learner. As a child I was put on the first available animal which came to hand, regardless of its temperament. I learned very quickly to adjust. With this one you will need to keep a firmer rein and a strict rule or he will take advantage of you.' He straightened, giving the animal a slap on the rump and turning to swing himself up on the black with practised ease.

The movement of the gelding was different, Lian found: not as smooth as the mare's, and certainly not as comfortable. It was better when she sat right down into the saddle and let the movement carry her instead of trying to follow it. Now she could feel what he was going to do through her legs.

'Good,' Ricardo pronounced, watching her. 'Now you

begin to relax a little. Are you ready to go faster?'

What he really meant was had she the courage to go faster, Lian thought, and gritted her teeth. She would show him!

'Yes,' she said.

'Then come.' Dark eyes glinting, he put his mount straight into a canter, the change of pace followed immediately by the gelding without any direction whatsoever. Holding on to the reins like grim death, Lian concentrated on staying on the animal, willing her body to find the rhythm. And suddenly it was there, sticking her to the saddle as if she had been born to it, easing out the tension and bringing blood-tingling enjoyment of the flying passage over grassland blue with alfalfa on which the cattle fed. Almost without realising it, she found the stride had lengthened into a gallop, the black drawing ahead as though pulled by invisible chains. Instinctively she increased the pressure of knee and thigh, and felt the gelding surge forward in response. There was small chance of overtaking Diablo, but she could give Ricardo a run for his money!

She was sorry when the black began slowing down, but she obeyed Ricardo's sign to rein in. The gelding was blowing a bit by the time they came down to a walk again, but seemed to have enjoyed the race as much as she had, judging from his skittish lightness of step. Ricardo was smiling.

'You have a natural seat,' he said. 'José has been wasting his time taking you so slowly.'

'I suppose he thought my being English might make me timid,' she responded. Her eyes were sparkling, her cheeks flushed with colour from the breeze created by their passage. 'That was wonderful! I don't remember the last time I enjoyed anything as much!'

Mockery sprang in the line of his mouth. 'Your education has been neglected, little one, if you must rely on a gallop across the *pampas* for your greatest pleasure. Did no man ever make love to you?'

'Not wholly, no.' She refused to look at him, aware of the sudden increase in her pulse rate. 'Would that please me more?'

'It would depend upon the man. He would need first to subdue you before he could begin to love you. Not all men would be capable of doing so.'

But he would, she thought on a swift wave of emotion. He had proved himself more than capable of it the night he had brought her to Mendoza. Only that had been in anger, not in desire. She remembered the feel of his lips against hers, the hardness of his hands, and felt a quiver run through her. She didn't want that again—did she?

'Where does all the water go?' she asked quickly. 'It rained three times this last week, but it never stays on the ground.'

'There are few depressions deep enough to hold it for longer than a few hours,' he said. 'The earth is porous enough to allow it to sink through almost immediately. That is why we need the wind pumps to draw it to the surface again, and the tanks to hold it. In the Sierra it is different. Up there you will find streams, even small lakes, because the rock holds the water above ground.'

Lian turned her gaze to where the distant hills cut the skyline, hazed and nebulous in the shimmering heat. 'Do you ever go there?'

'The Sierra?' He shrugged. 'Occasionally I have explored the defiles and valleys, but not for some time now.'

Because he dared not be away from Mendoza long enough to let Carlos get too strong a grip on it? she wondered. Aloud she said hesitantly, 'Would you allow me to go some time? I'd love to see it closer.'

'Alone, no. The hills might look close, but it would take you almost a day to reach them on horseback.'

'I can drive.'

'Undoubtedly. The answer is still no. It is only too easy to become lost up there. And a car has only limited power of access. To see the Sierras in any detail one must travel on horseback.' He paused, body easy in the saddle. 'Perhaps when the shipping is over we will make a short expedition— two days, or three.'

Her glance was swift. 'Just—the two of us?'

'Why not?' he returned dryly. 'In the eyes of the world we are man and wife. Who is to know or to care whether we sleep in two tents or one?'

Who indeed! On a surge of some nameless emotion she urged the gelding forward into a trot, lifting automatically in the stirrups.

'Sit down,' he called sharply. 'You are not in Rotten Row!'

Startled, she waited for him to come up, meeting his narrowed gaze. 'You know London?'

'I have been there. Only the ones who ride for show alone rise to the trot. You will please me by conforming to our style—or lack of it, as you prefer.'

'All right,' she said, and felt his mood change again.

'The soft answer turneth away wrath?' he quoted on a quizzical note.

'So it's said.' She paused before asking the obvious question. '*Were* you angry?'

'A little. You have a way of making me so.'

'I'm sorry.'

'No,' he said, 'you are not. If you regret anything it is only your first appeal to me that night in the Club Rios.'

She didn't deny it. 'There wasn't much alternative.'

'There is always an alternative. Not, in this case, one you would have liked any better, I think.'

'And certainly not made me as much profit!'

The animals were close enough for him to reach out a swift hard hand and close it vice-like about her upper arm, bringing both horses to a stop as he pulled her round bodily to face him. Her leg was squashed between warm hides, bound knee to calf against his. The pressure opened her mouth on a small sound of protest.

'One day you will go too far,' Ricardo said with dangerous

softness. 'I needed you, but I did not buy you.'

Lian was tremulous and in pain, but she refused to give way. 'What else would you call it?'

'A compensation, for the loss of your time and opportunity.'

'That's splitting hairs.'

'No.' His gaze seared. 'Had I *bought* you I would have claimed full possession of my property on our wedding night.'

'And lost your case for an annulment?'

'It would have made little difference. There are other ways and means of breaking a contract. Take care you do not provoke me to the need of finding them!'

She swallowed on sudden dryness. 'Ricardo——'

'Do not Ricardo me. It would be good for you to know submission to a man. Perhaps then you would respect.'

'I'd *hate* you!' she said with passion. 'If you touch me——'

'I am touching you now. If I take you, is what you mean to say.' His lips were curled. 'And you would do—what?'

'Try it and see!' she flung at him recklessly, and at once wished she hadn't as his expression changed.

'You challenge me?'

'No.' The dryness was back, husking her voice. Her eyes dropped from his. 'I didn't mean it like that.'

'I see. There are shades in your language that defeat me still, then.' The sarcasm bit. 'You wish to retract anything else you have said these last moments?'

'I suppose so.'

He shook her, causing the gelding to move a step or two forward and urging his own mount to keep pace without releasing her. 'You had *better* suppose so. And now!'

'All right, so I wasn't bought.' It was taking all she had in the way of nerve to hang on to the remnants of her pride. She lifted her head in defiance. 'I was hired. Is that any better?'

He remained as he was for a long moment looking down into her rigidly controlled face. 'You compromise with poor grace,' he said at last with a certain grimness. 'We must make sure that you practise more.' He let her go then, watching her rub the bruised flesh with the hardness still lingering about his mouth. 'You still wish to see the branding?'

'Providing you don't try to use it on me,' she said ruefully, and was rewarded by a glimmer of a smile, though without much humour.

'It is going to take more than a singeing to convince you, apparently. But convince you I will.'

Only not the way he had threatened, she told herself as he put Diablo into forward motion again. Whatever he said to the contrary, there could be no annulment once the marriage had been consummated, and any other way of dissolving it had to be more difficult. She was safe enough; of course she was safe enough. No amount of provocation would cause him to forget his own interests.

They came on the railhead after following one of the dirt roads for some distance. Tall wire fences enclosed large areas close by, the latter already holding a sizeable number of animals. There were ramps and pens for loading closer to the rail line itself, and a couple of tin-roofed huts. Dust hung over the scene, raised by a multitude of trampling hooves. There was a lot of noise, and a pungent smell of singed hair which wrinkled Lian's nostrils.

The animals still in need of marking with the Mendoza brand were herded together in a separate enclosure close by the glowing brazier, each one brought across singly as required. Lian watched a hornless beast with smooth black hide cut from the milling throng still waiting to be dealt with, and driven across to be roped by another *gaucho* and brought to its side in bellowing protest. The action was smooth and efficient, yet another man extracting the hot iron from the heart of the glowing brazier and bending to press it swiftly to the dusty black hide. Hair sizzled and smoked, yet surprisingly there seemed no particular increase in the animal's volume of bellows. The confining rope removed from its legs, it staggered indignantly upright, and needed no invitation to join its fellows in the larger enclosure.

The next animal singled out was also dusty, but there was no doubting its reddish colouring and white markings. Lian had seen the breed often enough in fields around home to be fairly sure of her ground.

'That's a Hereford!' she exclaimed in astonishment.

'It is,' Ricardo agreed. 'And the other was an Aberdeen Angus. Along with the Shorthorn, they constitute the greater part of Mendoza's stock. You know something of cattle?'

'Nothing—except that this kind don't give milk.' There was gratification in the glance she swept over the enclosures. 'You'll agree, then, that Britain has worthwhile products?'

'I have never said otherwise. The English financed the beginning of our meat-packing industry and gave us our railway system.'

'I hope it's better than ours!'

He laughed. 'From what I hear it would have to be, though we too suffer from nationalisation. As to the cattle, it is a long time since the first specimen herds were introduced. We have interbred with some of them to try to obtain the best combination of attributes, not always successfully.'

One of the men detached himself from the working group and came across, loose trousers tucked into a band at the ankle, white shirt covered by a short black sleeveless jacket. He removed his hat respectfully as Lian smiled at him.

'*Buenos días*, José,' she said cheerfully.

'*Buenos días, señora*,' he returned. If he was surprised by her being there he did not reveal it. He turned back to his employer and said something else, speaking too quickly for Lian to follow more than a word here and there. She registered something about sheep and fence, and saw Ricardo's features darken as he shot back a question.

'I will attend to it,' she understood him to say in the end, dismissing the foreman. Brusquely he indicated the horses, adding in English to Lian, 'We will return now.'

She waited until they were mounted and moving off before saying tentatively, 'Is there any trouble, Ricardo?'

'Not now, but there could have been had José not taken steps to rectify the matter. Some of the Riga sheep had broken through the east boundary fence on to Mendoza land. José had them driven back and repaired the gap.'

'Oh, I see.' She was relieved. 'No harm done, then.'

His expression did not lighten. 'José believes the fence was deliberately cut.'

She looked at him quickly. 'Who would do that?'

'Carlos might. He knows how I feel about sheep on Mendoza land.'

'Oh, but surely that would be a pretty futile gesture? I mean, with this amount of land it would take months for even hundreds of sheep to make any impression.'

The dark head shook impatiently. 'There is more at stake here than that. One or a thousand, it does not matter.'

Lian kept her voice carefully neutral. 'A principle, you mean?'

'That is right. Francisco must use his own land in the way he sees fit, but I will have none of his stock introduced to Mendoza.'

'But they could have been there by accident,' she argued. 'José could be wrong.'

'If José believes the wires were cut then there is little doubt about it,' he came back curtly. 'To whom would you prefer to give the benefit of the doubt—Carlos?'

Biting her lip, she said, 'I just can't see what he could hope to gain by it, that's all.'

'He does not have to gain anything in that sense. For Carlos it will be enough that he has contrived to break my taboos.'

They rode in silence for some moments before Lian said, 'So what happens now?'

He shrugged. 'I shall return you to the house, then take

the car and call on my half-brother with a warning.'

'A warning?'

'One he cannot fail to understand. The next time such a thing happens, if ever, I shall have the straying animals shot and returned to him as carcases.'

Lian drew in a breath. 'You wouldn't!'

'I would.' There was no doubting the implacability of that statement. He urged his mount onwards over the plain with grimly set features and she knew she had displeased him in her defence of Carlos. But someone had to stay rational in this matter.

There was little said between them after that until they reached the *casa*. Dismounting a little stiffly from the gelding, Lian walked with him to the cars, plucking up courage as he opened the door of the estate.

'Ricardo, take me with you,' she begged.

'No,' he said flatly, and got behind the wheel. 'You will stay here and wait my return.'

There was no arguing with that tone of voice—she had already learned that much. She watched helplessly as he put the car into motion and swept away towards the gates.

CHAPTER FIVE

LIAN ate lunch alone in the white-walled *comedor*, sitting in state at one end of the long dark table. Juanita brought in coffee, her smile still shy, her manner reticent. Lian thanked her in Spanish and wished she could be allowed to make a friend of her. The house servants here were very well treated, but rigid protocol was observed at all times. Certainly no mere *camerera* would dream of taking liberties.

Afterwards there was little to do but wait for Ricardo to return. When the car did come into view, she was sitting under the cedar nearest to the stone arch under which it must pass, her back against the trunk, arms wrapped about her bent knees. He stopped alongside, eyeing her with lifted brows.

'Is there no comfort indoors, that you must sit out here like a waif?' he queried.

'I was bored,' she said as she came to her feet. 'The servants leave me nothing to do.' She stopped a foot or so away from the opened window, trying to judge his mood from his face and failing miserably as usual. 'How did it go?'

'How would you expect it to have gone? There was no fight, if that is what you were hoping to hear.'

Her head jerked in protest. 'I have no wish for you and Carlos to fight. Why should I have?'

'To relieve your boredom, perhaps. A family feud is always entertaining to those not involved.'

'Except that Carlos isn't family in the true sense of the word, according to what you believe,' she came back. 'A love child—isn't that the polite term?'

The olive features had darkened. 'Lust would be the more appropriate word. And that is not a subject I will discuss with you out here. Get into the car.'

'It's hardly any distance up to the house,' she protested. 'I can walk.' She held the dark gaze for a moment longer, then gave a small sigh and moved to obey. How was it, she wondered, that within moments of meeting again she and Ricardo were on opposite sides? She hadn't meant to say what she had about Carlos—that was rubbing salt into the wounds with a vengeance. Yet something in her would not allow complete regret. Ricardo wasn't wholly in the right in this situation. It was too complex a matter to be decided on the basis of upon which side of the blanket each of the brothers had been born.

'Have you eaten yet?' she asked when they reached the house. 'I wanted to wait, but Inez insisted on serving lunch on the hour.'

'Inez was right. She did not know when I would be back.' He came round to open her door as she continued to sit there waiting. 'It is something to know you are learning to accept the small courtesies a man expects to pay a woman,' he added with satire. 'Only a few days ago you would have been out of your seat before I could move from mine.'

'Only a few days ago I was still in possession of some initiative,' she responded, borrowing his tone. 'You seem to have sapped that too.'

'Too?' He pounced on the word, eyes narrowing as he looked down at her from his extra six inches of height. 'Which other quality have you lost since coming here to Mendoza?'

'I don't know.' She put up a hand and brushed her hair from her face, avoiding his eyes. 'I was just talking for the sake of it, I suppose. You make me say things I don't mean to say.'

'No one can do that. But I am willing to concede that you do not always say what you mean.' He turned towards the house as if to dismiss the subject, leaving her to follow a step behind in what, she thought ruefully, he probably considered her rightful place.

Thinking about it, she wondered just what she had meant by that enigmatic remark. Something deep down inside her had prompted it, some instinct over which she had no control. A part of her mind shied away from isolating the emotion too completely.

Inez came hurrying to greet the master of the house, her attitude, as always, quite different in his presence.

'I have already eaten,' he advised her when she asked his requirements. 'But we will have coffee brought out.'

Lian opened her mouth to say she had already drunk coffee, then closed it again abruptly. Why bother? She could always drink some more. In this mood, Ricardo was best gone along with—humoured, you might say. She wished she knew what had transpired at the Riga home.

There was little shade out in the courtyard at this hour of the day. The old man Lian knew as Enrico crossed it slowly, body bent with age and with constant stooping over a lifetime of cultivation. The beauty of the *casa* surrounds owed much to this man, and would continue to owe it to his son when he was gone. The people who served the estate regarded it as their home just as much as any Mendoza, Lian had come to learn. The same three families had provided the whole of the house staff for as long back as anyone could remember. All families had their own smallholding within the boundaries of the *estancia*, each individual plot fenced by wire where necessary to separate it from its neighbours; the result a regular *mestizo* township some mile or so distant from the *casa* itself. Lian had seen the white adobe dwellings from a distance but not ventured too close, recognising their right to privacy. She doubted if they lived in anything approaching luxury, but they seemed more than happy with their lot. Who was she, as a stranger, to rate the quality of that contentment?

It was almost with surprise that she had heard herself asking, 'Did you see Isabella?' and watching his face in the shadow cast by the archway under which they sat as she did so. If there was a reaction he immediately concealed it, but then she would have expected no less.

'I saw Isabella,' he said. 'She sends her regards to you, and her hopes that you are adjusting to the many differences between this land and your own.'

'Isabella has perception.'

'She is a woman,' he retorted dryly, and she gave him a swift glance from beneath her lashes.

'You'll allow we might have things in common?'

'Beneath the veneer applied by the separate cultures you are both in possession of the same basic instincts. That much you have both of you proved.'

Lian kept her voice level. 'If you mean what I think you mean, it's called "having an eye to the main chance". Do you think Isabella only married Carlos because she believed he was to have the estate? If that were true she could have gained the same result by marrying you.'

'She was not asked to marry me,' he said harshly. 'And you have said enough.'

She had said more than enough, Lian acknowledged wryly. He had loved Isabella and lost her to his half-brother, and along with her he had almost lost the *estancia*. He needed no reminder.

The coffee had gone cold in her cup, but she drank it anyway, conscious of tension in the air. The wrought iron table felt solid beneath her hand, its width and substance a symbol of the barrier between them. She wanted suddenly to reach across it, to touch the brown hand lying like her own on its surface. This man was her husband, yet she held no real place in his life. What would it take, she wondered, to stir him?

She caught herself up there on an edge of panic. Was she

crazy? The last thing she wanted was emotional involvement —of any kind.

'Will you be going to La Plata with the stock?' she asked into the silence.

He shook his head. 'There is no need. My contract with the company owning the *frigorífico* is already set. The terms, however, are due for review after this shipment. I am to meet with my buyers next week in Santina for this purpose.'

'Will you be bringing them back here?'

'No. This is purely a business affair, and I am not in the mood for entertaining.'

Because of her? The fewer people who knew the better, she supposed. She said hesitantly, 'Then may I come into Santina with you? I could look around the town while you conducted your business with these people.'

'I think not. Santina is no place for a woman on her own.'

'Why?' she demanded in frustration. 'Because she might be mistaken for something she isn't?'

'If you wish.' Eyes glinting, he added, 'Those who put themselves in the way of insult should not be surprised when the insult occurs. I would have imagined one occasion more than enough for you.'

'That was different. You know it was. I'd be outside in broad daylight.'

'And flaunting that colouring of yours for all to note and and covet.'

She flared, 'I do not flaunt!'

'Purposely, perhaps not. But you draw attention, and the Latin is not slow to react to the merest hint of opportunity.' His smile mocked. 'You need a man to protect you from such advances, and I shall not be available. Later, when the transaction has been completed, I shall take you to Santina. In the meantime you will do as I bid you and stay at home.'

'This isn't my home,' she said with bitterness. 'I don't even have the freedom of a guest!'

His shrug was indifferent. 'There is more to freedom than the ability to roam at will. You take *siesta* now?'

The familiar stillness and silence of mid-afternoon already reigned, the courtyard empty of all but the motionless plants. Even the latter seemed to droop as though in contemplation.

'I can't sleep in the middle of the day,' Lian said.

'You do not have to sleep, merely to rest during this part of it.'

'I've known it as hot as this in England, and nobody takes to their bed halfway through the day because of it.'

He looked at her for a long reflective moment. 'You are trying to annoy me,' he stated at length. 'We are coming to the end of our hotter months here in the *pampas*. In England you are fortunate to have two consecutive days of consistent temperatures in the whole of your normal summers. Work begins here long before your shops and offices come alive. *Siesta* is not an indulgence but a recuperation of the body and mind at a time when they are at their most fatigued.' The pause was brief. 'I must insist that you pander to the habits of the household and retire to your room until four o'clock.'

She met his gaze without bothering to conceal her resentment. 'For my own good, I suppose.'

'Surprisingly, yes.'

'But the rule doesn't apply to you, of course.'

His gaze hardened. 'I am my own master. Do you do as you are told, or must I make you?'

What he really wanted was to be rid of her, Lian acknowledged numbly. She stood up without further protest and left him.

Lying on her bed in the pleasant dimness of her room, she wondered what he would do with the next hour himself. Read, perhaps—or even just sit and think. Would she figure in those thoughts at all, or would he deliberately turn himself off from the cold reality of his marriage? Had it been real they might have spent the afternoon together, talking companionably—or even making love. Ricardo would be another kind of man with a woman he loved, she thought. He would cherish her, protect her, possess her in every sense of the word. With such love no woman would resent that possession. It would be a part of it; part of him. To be loved by Ricardo . . .

She turned over and desperately thumped the pillow in its satin day cover back into shape, trying to rid her mind and her heart of the aching emptiness. Ricardo would never love her; she wouldn't want him to. There was nothing, *nothing* that could bring them together.

The cattle were loaded for shipment two mornings later, herded through the confining pens and up the ramps into the waiting trucks in bellowing protest. Lian had accepted Ricardo's invitation to accompany him to the railhead again with cautious pleasure, disregarding the earliness of the hour.

Rising in the delightful coolness of the Argentinian morning presented no hardship. It was the best time of all for a ride across the *pampa*, the air fresh and clean, the distances stretching to the ends of the earth beneath a sky streaked high and wide with feathers of cloud. Riding had become her favourite pastime. She loved the feel of silk-clad muscles between her knees, the smell of warm leather and horsehide in her nostrils. She had tried out other of the Estancia horses over the last couple of days, but still preferred the gelding she had ridden that first time out. His Spanish name was Rojo, in reference to the warm red-brown of his coat. Lian had taken to grooming him herself, finding pleasure in putting an extra sheen on the glossy hide. No one else had ridden him since she had shown interest, whether by accident or design she had yet to discover.

Ricardo looked across at her now with a faint smile as she watched the scene of activity. She was wearing jodhpurs which had once been his mother's, and which were a little old-fashioned in cut but infinitely kinder on the legs than her own jeans, plus a white roll-necked sweater with the sleeves pushed halfway up her arms. Tendrils of hair had escaped from below the brim of her hat, lifting in the breeze about a face bare of make-up but for a touch of pale pink lipstick.

'You have changed,' he said unexpectedly. 'You look very different from the girl I first saw in the Club Rios that night.'

'For better or worse?' she asked lightly, and heard him laugh.

'For better, naturally, or I would not be saying it. No man should comment on a woman's looks unless he can say something complimentary.'

'Not all men think the way you do.'

'Not all men are Argentinian,' he agreed, the smile still etching his lips. 'You think perhaps the Latin has his good points?'

'I think definitely the Latin knows the way to a woman's heart,' she returned, and could have bitten her tongue as she saw the slow lift of the mobile brow.

'If she has a heart then he may well reach it,' he said with irony. 'You wear yours far from your sleeve, *chica*.'

Lian hoped so. There was no accounting for its reaction these days. Looking at him now she felt the familiar tension gathering inside her. The times when she could forget the nature of their relationship were few and far between. Often she tried to imagine herself at the other end of the six months, wondering what her reactions to leaving this place would be. A part of her couldn't wait for the day to come, while another part shied away from the finality of it. Could one live with another person for so long and steer clear of all involvement in their lives?

'I'm hungry,' she said quickly. 'Are you coming back for breakfast, or are you staying to see the loading finished?'

'I will return with you,' he said. 'José can take care of things here. With the shipping done I can afford to relax a little from the pressure.' He paused before adding softly, 'You still find life at the *casa* so boring?'

Lian had the grace to flush. 'Boring was the wrong word to use in the first place. Frustrating might be a better one.

Apart from riding and reading, I'm left with little to do. Inez won't allow me even to make my own bed.'

'She perhaps does not find your method satisfactory.' His tone was dry. 'Inez has been in total charge of organising the household for so long she would naturally find it difficult to relinquish any part of it.'

Especially to someone like her, Lian thought with a pang. Aloud, and with deliberate lightness, she said, 'I suppose if I were your real wife she——'

'You *are* my *real* wife,' he cut in with a thin smile. 'Legally, if not emotionally. For the present you have the right, if you desire it, to take over any part of Inez's duties should you choose. All you have to do is to tell her.'

'She wouldn't listen.'

'It is up to you to see that she listens.'

'Is it?' She leaned forward to rub the space between Rojo's ears, voice low. 'Does Inez know that we aren't—that we don't spend the nights together?'

'I have never discussed it with her,' Ricardo said coolly. 'I imagine the use of two rooms without a connecting door may have given all the house servants food for thought. I should have taken that lack into consideration when deciding the location of our quarters. On the east side of the house are those used by my parents, complete with the door I mentioned. You would prefer to save face by moving there?'

The jeer brought her chin up. 'It's a bit late for that. Don't married couples ever share a room in this country?'

'It is a matter of choice. Many prefer to retain the subtle stimulation of parting after making love; the provocation of the separate bed. Should they wish on occasion to spend the whole of the night together that choice is open to them too.'

Lian longed to ask which would be his own preference, but couldn't pluck up the nerve. 'You said they,' she said instead. 'Don't you really mean *he*?'

'You suggest an Argentinian wife has no option but to submit to the demands of a husband?'

'Well, has she?'

'Shall we say any man so unskilled in the art of arousing a woman as to gain a denial merits no better.'

'And no Latin, of course, would lack that skill!'

He leaned forward without warning to grasp the gelding's reins close up by the bit and bring the animal to a halt along with his own mount. There was a dangerous glint in the dark eyes. 'Are you trying to provoke me into making love to you?'

She held his gaze without flinching, hoping he could not hear the thud of her heart. 'If I provoke you at all it's only because you lead me into it. I think you do it purposely.'

The smile was slow and unexpected. 'You may be right in that. I hope one day to teach you the rudiments of discretion.' He let go of the rein and straightened in the saddle. 'Try to remember, *chica*, for your own sake if not for mine. Our time together can be pleasant enough with a little effort.'

All of which must come from her, Lian surmised, and knew a sense of futility. Could it really make any difference to the way things were?

The weekend brought a storm of impressive proportions, with rainfall so heavy it was impossible to venture out of doors without becoming immediately soaked to the skin. Ricardo explained the cause of such extreme weather conditions as due to the movement of dense polar air and warm tropical air together. It was certainly by no means an unusual occurrence.

'We are in a temperate zone here in the *pampa*,' he said. 'It never becomes too uncomfortably hot during the summers, nor too cold in the winter, apart from the few days when we may have frost. It is a good climate in which to live and work.'

Winter would be more than halfway gone when the time came for her to leave, Lian realised. Somehow that thought served to make the day seem even further off. It would be autumn in England when she eventually arrived home. That seemed symbolic too, though of what she wasn't quite sure.

Ricardo left for Santina on the Monday morning, having arranged to spend the night there. Lian could only guess at the sums involved in these transactions, but knew they must be enormous. She had made no further mention of accompanying him to the town, and been rewarded with a promise of a visit the following week.

The day seemed over-long in the knowledge that he would not be returning at all. Sometimes he was gone from the *casa* for several hours during the day, often he was engaged with his managers for a large part of it, but for these last few nights he had shown no inclination to relieve himself of her company after they had eaten dinner, staying instead to drink a leisurely brandy and talk, to smoke a cheroot while they listened together to his extensive collection of records.

Once or twice Lian had caught him watching her with a faintly quizzical expression, as though wondering when her former aggression would re-emerge. Often it simmered just below the surface, but she carefully damped it down again. Learning the finesse of handling a man like Ricardo Mendoza wasn't easy, yet she found herself beginning to take a kind of pleasure in it. A dangerous kind of pleasure, she acknowledged on occasion, yet the alternative of constant friction served no safer purpose.

She spent the morning diligently improving her Spanish with the aid of a dictionary Ricardo had found for her. She could make herself understood in most things with the servants now, although she found difficulty sometimes in understanding the local dialect spoken by almost all. The differences were not so much in the words themselves as in intonation and emphasis. Juanita helped her where she could, her shyness receded a little over the weeks.

As had become her custom, she read and dozed through the afternoon hours, stretched out on a lounger within the shade of the courtyard until it was time to change for her second ride of the day. Rojo was ready saddled when she went out to the stables. Diablo had been turned out into the smaller of the two corrals, standing quietly in the sunlight with black coat gleaming, the magnificent head lifted to sniff the wind. He was waiting for Ricardo too, Lian thought; missing him even as she missed him. He dominated them both without effort, and left them yearning for more.

When she called softly to the stallion he turned his head her way but made no move towards the fence where she stood, his regard disdainful. One day, she promised herself recklessly, she would ride him. She had plenty of time—more than five months of it. Time for anything.

It was gone six when she got back to the *casa*. She went in from the rear through the courtyard intending to use the outer staircase to reach her bedroom. The man sitting at the wrought iron table under the curve of the middle arch came slowly to his feet as she came into view, his face expressing astonishment.

'Señora Mendoza?' he queried on a note of doubt.

'Yes.' Lian could still hardly believe it either. The new-comer was English right through, the brownish hair worn casually styled about a square featured, attractively rugged face, his slacks and safari-style jacket comfortably cut. Her smile was sudden and dazzling in its welcome. 'Hallo!'

He smiled back, though still with an element of uncertainty. 'Hallo! I'm Grant Edwards, a friend of Ricardo's. I seem to have chosen a bad time to come visiting.'

'No, you haven't,' she assured him swiftly. 'It's wonderful to see someone from home! I'm Lian. Do sit down again. I see they've already given you a drink.'

He pulled a wry face. 'With some reservations. I was met at the door by an old battleaxe in a black dress who didn't want to let me in at all. She said Ricardo was away on business. At least, that's how I understood it.' The grin came freely. 'Can't see why these folk can't learn English like everybody else. It's a darn sight easier to comprehend.'

Lian laughed, leaning her elbows on the back of a chair

as she looked across at him. 'Inez isn't so bad when you get to know her. She just doesn't care for strangers, that's all. I think she imagines they all want to steal the silver.'

'There's enough of it,' he agreed easily. 'It's quite a place, isn't it?'

'Oh, yes, it's quite a place.'

It was his turn to laugh. 'Typical British comment, what? Seriously though, I can't quite take it in that you're Ricardo's wife. He never mentioned he was married when I saw him a couple of months back.'

'He wasn't,' she said. 'Not then.' She kept the smile firmly in place. 'We were married only two weeks ago in Buenos Aires. Do you live in Argentina, Grant?'

'At present. I'm up in the Chaco. Oil,' he added, seeing her blank look. 'Advisory capacity in opening up a new field.'

'Is that where you met Ricardo?'

'No, that was in Rio. I'd flown down for a long weekend, Somebody introduced us and we seemed to hit it off pretty well. Before I left he suggested I pay the Estancia a visit on my next leave. I had a couple of weeks or so due, so I decided to take him up on it.' His tone was rueful. 'I should have contacted him first, I suppose, instead of just dropping in like this, only it's the way things are done in this country. I drove in from the airstrip in Santina, so I can easily go back there for the night and get a flight out tomorrow.'

'You can't do that without at least seeing Ricardo,' Lian responded at once. 'I'll have a room prepared for you. He'll be back in the morning. As a matter of fact, he's in Santina himself.'

'He is? I might even have spotted him then if I'd come through the town, only I cut straight across from the airfield once I'd fixed up a car, to avoid getting snarled up. These marketing centres can get pretty crowded.' He paused, the doubt still in his expression. 'Look, I can't muscle in at a time like this. You must only just be back off your honeymoon.'

'We didn't have one,' she said without thinking, and felt herself warm before the sudden speculation in his gaze. 'There was no time for a proper one,' she tagged on hurriedly, not even sure if the British concept of a honeymoon held any bearing here. 'Ricardo had to be back for the shipping out, and to see his buyers. Things should be a little less hectic now until the next shipment comes up.' She looked up as Inez appeared silently from within the house, steeling herself to take her rightful position as mistress, no matter on how temporary a basis. 'Señor Edwards will be staying, tonight, at least,' she said in Spanish. 'Please have a room prepared for him.'

The housekeeper stiffened almost imperceptibly. 'The master——' she began.

'Señor Edwards is here at his invitation,' Lian interrupted smoothly. 'And would you ask Juanita to bring us some tea.'

Grant looked at her in some admiration as the other departed. 'You certainly know how to handle her,' he said.

Lian had surprised herself at how easy it was once the initial barrier against giving orders was overcome. Inez did not respond to being asked in hesitant tones to do something; she was used to authority. Small wonder that Ricardo had been so impatient with her former lack of that quality. To him it came so naturally.

'Tell me about your work,' she said, taking a seat alongside him. 'Is it interesting?'

'Depends on how you look at it. Conditions are fairly primitive up there, and the local labour situation could be better. Apart from that it's all experience.'

'You're a freelance?'

'No. I'm on loan from my company.'

'Married?' she hazarded, and he smiled and shook his head. 'This isn't the kind of a job a man could do with a wife and kids to think about. Wouldn't even see them half the year. I aim to make my pile before I settle down. I've made thirty-five my deadline—that gives me another six years.'

'What happens if you meet a girl you want to marry before that?' Lian asked on a light note. 'Are you going to ask her to wait for you?'

'Shouldn't think so. I'd have to rethink, maybe.' He looked at her. 'Seems these things can happen pretty quickly.'

Her own eyes dropped. 'Yes, they can.'

Darkness had fallen with its usual swiftness, the sky turning from soft opacity to deep velvet in bare moments, the stars already sprinkled thickly. The night sounds were too familiar now to impinge upon the conscious mind; they were there as an accepted background, only notable if they had ceased. Juanita's pretty gurgling laugh came from the direction of the kitchens, followed by a man's deeper tones raised in admonition. Softly, from some distance away, came the plaintive notes of a guitar idly plucked.

Grant drew in a contented breath. 'Peaceful here, isn't it? Makes a pleasant change from where I come from. Which part of England did you live?'

'London,' she told him, and knew a swift pang of homesickness. February in England: cold; damp; possibly foggy, but at that moment she wanted it with everything in her.

'Hey!' he exclaimed in gratified tones, 'I'm a Londoner too—at least I was born there. Eighteen months since I last saw it. How long since you left?'

There was little point, Lian decided, in trying to concoct a story. She was sure to let herself down in some detail later on, and he would think that even stranger than the truth.

'Almost three weeks,' she said, and forced herself to meet his eyes and smile at his expression. 'I know—it seems unbelievable to me too. I was stranded after being let down by the dancing troupe I was supposed to join in Buenos Aires when Ricardo found me. We were married two days later.'

He looked at her with uncertainty. 'Well, I knew the Latin was capable of swift decisions, but this beats all! You must have been very sure of your feelings for him.'

The temptation to spill out the whole story was great. Lian

resisted it with an effort. Her shrug and laugh was convincingly easy. 'Ricardo is not a man one refuses.'

His gaze narrowed. 'You mean you married him for his money?'

'Is that so hard to believe?'

'Yes,' he said after a moment. 'Yes, it is. You're not the gold-digging type. Are you trying to tell me you don't love him?'

She bit her lip. The question was too direct for prevarication, nor did she think herself capable of pretending to such an emotion in any way likely to convince this man. 'Don't judge me, Grant,' she pleaded. 'There are things about my marriage I can't discuss. I've already said far too much.'

Juanita brought out the tea at that moment, to her relief. By the time the girl had set out the crockery and departed she was sufficiently in command of herself to lift the teapot with a steady hand.

'Cream?' she asked.

'Please. And two sugars.' He waited until she had passed him the cup before making any attempt to return to their previous conversation. 'Look,' he said frankly, 'you can tell me to mind my own business if you like, but we're both English and that makes me feel in some way concerned in all this.' He hesitated before saying it. 'Did Ricardo use any form of coercion to get you to marry him?'

'No.' The denial was too swift, and she knew it. She gave him a look of appeal. 'I should never have told you any of it. I don't know what made me.'

'I do,' he said. 'You needed somebody, and these people are Ricardo's, not yours. I was tremendously flattered when you gave me such a welcome just now. Knowing the reason, I can see why you'd be glad to see anybody who wasn't of Spanish blood.' He paused, then added with some deliberation, 'I can also understand Ricardo's speed in snapping you up. You're a very beautiful girl, Lian. The kind a lot of men would lose their heads over. But he should have given you more time to know your own mind.'

His assumption was natural under the circumstances, she realised. He was taking it that Ricardo had fallen and fallen hard for her and swept her along on the wave of his own passion before she had chance to think about the long-term values of their relationship. It was a long way from the truth, but it was infinitely better than the mire into which her own half-truths had led her. Grant Edwards was Ricardo's friend. She must do nothing more to undermine that friendship, simply to gain a temporary ally. She was still on her own.

CHAPTER SIX

LIAN enjoyed dinner eaten in Grant's company. He was an entertaining partner, making her laugh with some of the tales he had to tell of the things that went wrong in his line of work.

'We've hit more snags with this field than I've ever come up against before,' he acknowledged ruefully. 'If this second hole comes up dry too I shall start thinking we're not meant to find it.'

'You sure it's there at all?' Lian queried, and he shrugged.

'As sure as anyone can be in this game. Wouldn't be the first time I'd been led up a gumtree.' They had retired to the *salón* for coffee and brandy. Now he sat back in his seat and eyed the deep soft amber liquid through the glass with satisfaction. 'This is the life! I miss the refinements up there.' His gaze came back to her sitting opposite, taking in the natural grace of her own relaxed pose, the slender curving lines of her body beneath the simple yellow dress. 'You said you were a dancer before you married Ricardo. Don't you miss it?'

'A little,' Lian was bound to admit. 'Not as much as I might have if I'd ever made it to the top, though.' She smiled. 'Being outside of it has given me the chance to assess my capabilities rather more accurately than when I was actually doing it. I'm not a bad dancer, but I'd never be a great one. It would have meant settling for mediocrity.'

'Whereas here you're queen of the whole castle.' His tone was light, without malice. 'Mistress of Mendoza!'

But only for as long as the master needed her. Lian fought

down the despondency of that knowledge. What did she have to complain about? She would be returning to England the richer by fifteen thousand pounds—enough to make her fairly independent of the need to find full-time work. The memory of these months here in the Argentine would eventually fade. She would meet someone else and make a real marriage. But she knew she lied to herself. This affair would be with her for always, colouring all other attachments.

'Shall we have some music?' she said a little desperately, and got to her feet to provide some, choosing a record at random from the cabinet. Only the lamps at this end of the *salón* were lit, creating an intimate atmosphere which lent itself only too well to the sultry rumba rhythm of the first number. It was one Ricardo had played the other night, she recalled: a selection of Latin-American music conducted by the band-leader Xavier Cugat. 'I like our rhythms,' he had commented lazily. 'There is something of the primitive in them which stirs both the mind and the sense. Do you feel the response pulsing through your body?' Lian had, and did now. Quite involuntarily she took a couple of gliding steps, turning with a small, half-embarrassed laugh to look back to where Grant sat watching her.

'It gets to you, doesn't it? Or don't you find it so?'

'Yes,' he said, 'I do.' He came to his feet, setting the brandy balloon down on the nearby table and straightening the jacket of his pale fawn suit. He was smiling, eyes frankly appreciative. 'You move like a dancer. Can't claim to be any expert myself, but I'd enjoy trying this one with you. Any objections to dancing with me?'

The hesitation was brief enough to be almost non-existent. Smile light and warm, she shook her head. 'I'd like that.'

He came to her, sliding an arm about her in the approved manner and taking her hand. He was roughly the same height as Ricardo, but somewhat bulkier in build. Seen in close-up, his skin was a little rough beneath the tan, the face of a man who had spent a great deal of his life in the open air in all conditions. Yet Ricardo's was smooth—olive smooth. She had yet to see him even in need of a shave. Not surprising really, considering the circumstances. Such ablutions were taken care of in the privacy of his own rooms. Only a real wife would ever know the peculiar delight of that particular intimacy.

'I thought you said you weren't very good,' she said after a moment or two of silence.

'You make it easy.' Almost imperceptibly his arm had tightened, drawing her a fraction closer. 'You're lovely to hold, Lian.' There was an element of wistfulness in his tone. 'It's been an age since I last danced with a girl I could communicate with properly.'

She said softly, 'You should go back home, Grant, and find yourself a wife. Don't leave it too late.'

'What about my six-year plan?' he came back on a light note. 'It takes money to keep a wife and raise a family.'

'Plenty do it on a average income without too much difficulty.'

'Not my style. I need an above average bank balance before I even start looking.'

'But if you're so lonely in this line of work——'

He laughed, sounding faintly forced. 'I don't normally give it much thought. It's being here with you like this that's doing it. Talking to you; watching you; touching you—well, it makes me realise what's missing, that's all. A week back in the Chanco and I'll be okay again.'

'You're too practical,' she said. 'You can't set out your life in neat little boxes. Things have a way to stepping in and upsetting the best of plans.'

'Like meeting someone and marrying them inside two days?' The words were spoken half jokingly, yet with an undercurrent of still unsatisfied curiosity. 'You know, you're not going to persuade me you're totally happy here. There's a certain look comes into your eyes whenever I mention Ricardo.'

She kept her gaze on the line of his mouth, watching the movement of his lips as he spoke with an odd sense of detachment. 'You're very perceptive for a man.'

'Maybe because I feel some kind of kinship with you. We neither of us belong here.' He paused. 'Are you afraid of him?'

'Would I have married a man I was afraid of?'

'You might under certain circumstances.'

She stopped as the music changed, dropping her hand from his shoulder. 'Grant, we've known one another barely four hours, and you hardly know Ricardo any better. We shouldn't be talking like this.'

'Time has nothing to do with it,' he said. 'I feel as though I've known you all my life. If that sounds idiotic, I can't help it. I'm your friend; I hope you're mine. I liked Ricardo when I met him, but that doesn't mean I'm ready to see nothing but good in him. He's a man, and we're all of us susceptible to temptation.'

She stared at him for a long moment before the penny dropped. 'You think I might have married him because I felt I had to?' she said at last. 'Wouldn't that be rather an outdated attitude these days?'

'Not for you,' he insisted. 'I think you're the kind with enough old-fashioned morality to believe you had to marry the first man who made love to you whether you loved him or not.'

'With that kind of morality he would have had to make love to me against my will,' she pointed out. 'Do you see Ricardo as a rapist?'

'No, but I'll bet he's a great persuader.' He touched her hair. 'The Latin goes overboard for colouring like yours!'

'Apparently not only the Latin,' came the clipped tones from the doorway, and Lian took a hasty step backwards away from Grant as Ricardo himself came further into the room.

'I—We didn't hear the car,' she stammered.

'No?' The irony crackled. 'Perhaps because you were not expecting it.' His glance moved to Grant standing a little awkwardly to one side, lips forming a cool smile of greeting. 'I am glad you did not forget my invitation. It was fortunate that I decided to return home tonight instead of waiting until tomorrow.'

Fortunate for whom? Lian wondered numbly. It was obvious from his attitude that he placed no great blame on Grant for the scene he had come upon. She was the culprit in allowing herself to come so close to another man, and she was the one who would bear the brunt of the anger simmering beneath that controlled exterior once he had her alone. For the moment nothing must come before the welcoming of a guest, no matter how inopportune.

Grant was looking uncomfortable and uncertain, as if wondering whether to try explaining away the apparent intimacy of his touch. Perhaps wisely he decided against it.

'Sorry to descend on you like this,' he said. 'I should have contacted you first to make sure it was all right.'

'There was no need. The invitation was for any time you cared to take it up.' If there had been any condemnation of the newcomer at all it was quite gone now. 'You are very welcome to stay as long as you wish. Lian, you have made our guest comfortable?'

She looked him in the eye, registering but refusing to acknowledge the sarcasm. 'Inez prepared a room on the far side of the courtyard from ours. Señor Edwards has already seen it.'

'*Señor* Edwards?' The strong mouth twisted. 'Come, you are both of you English. Such formality is surely unnecessary. The brandy is to your liking, Grant, or would you prefer something else?'

'No, I'm fine, thanks.' The other man moved back to his seat with an air of reassurance, satisfied that everything was all right. 'It's a great brandy.'

'A good one, I would say. The best we save for special occasions.' Ricardo moved across to pour himself a measure, returning to take a seat beside but a foot or two from Lian. The gaze he directed down into his glass was enigmatic. 'We must make tomorrow one of those occasions in honour of your visit, as I could not be present at dinner tonight. My return was not planned, as my wife has already intimated. How long a leave do you have?'

'A couple of weeks,' Grant told him. 'But I don't expect——'

'That is not very long,' interrupted the other smoothly. 'But we will do our best to make your stay as entertaining as we can. I may be engaged on business matters a part of each day, though I am sure you will find Lian a more than adequate hostess.' He settled himself more comfortably. 'Tell me about the oil business. Do you find any yet?'

Lian let the voices of the two men wash round her and over her for the next twenty minutes or so, making the occasional necessary response when brought into the conversation, but for the most part not really listening. On the surface Ricardo seemed totally calm and collected, but she knew him too well by now to be deceived by outward signs. The incident was not forgotten, only relegated to another time. Ricardo Mendoza neither forgot nor forgave anything easily.

She stood the tension for as long as she could before finally giving way.

'I hope you'll both excuse me if I leave you to it,' she said with a smile as she got up.

Both men rose with her; the olive face was expressionless. 'We will neither of us be lingering for long,' he said. 'Grant will be weary himself after his journey.'

'That's right,' agreed the other at once. He gave Lian a quick meaningful look. 'Goodnight, then. And thanks for looking after me the way you have.'

Every word was like a nail in her coffin, but he wasn't to know that, of course. So far as Grant was concerned there was no misunderstanding at all. So far as *he* was concerned, she thought wryly, he was right.

She went to her room quickly, passing Inez in the hall with a murmured '*Buenas noches*' unsmilingly answered. The housekeeper didn't like her any better than when she had first arrived, that was obvious. She was a usurper—a necessary evil—and as such to be despised. She might even have guessed that Ricardo was paying her to help him. How else could he have persuaded an English girl to spend the essential six months cut from her own people—cut off even from Ricardo himself? The woman hated her and made no secret of it. She would be glad to see the back of her when the time came. Everyone here would be glad—with the possible exception of Juanita.

Lian had not been particularly sleepy when she made her excuses, and the warm shower took away all inclination. With a cotton wrap pulled on over her nightdress she stood just inside the opened balcony doors, smelling the myriad scents and letting the night breeze play over her. When the outer door opened without any preliminary knock she froze, too well aware that only one person would enter her room without first seeking permission; one person angry enough to deem such courtesies undeserved.

Ricardo closed the door again quietly and stood for a moment with his back to it viewing her across the width of the room. She had turned out all the lamps before opening the windows, and was glad of it now. Moonlight was kinder in that it hid something of her feelings.

'You have something to say to me?' he queried on a silky note. 'Some explanation of your behaviour, perhaps?'

'Why should I bother when you've already made up your

mind about what you saw?' Lian retorted in low but clear
tones. 'I don't suppose it would occur to you that Grant might
have been making a pass at *me*?'

'Of course it would occur to me. He is a man, and there is
nothing more natural than for a man to respond to such
invitation.'

'Invitation?'

'Your closeness. Your obvious willingness to feel the touch
of his hands.'

'That's not fair!' she flung back. 'We were only close
because we'd been dancing, and he only touched my hair.'

'If you had, as you say, been dancing then he must have
touched a great deal more than your hair.' The control was
being deliberately dropped. 'You must have put on the
record, therefore you were the one who wanted to dance. Did
he excite you, this countryman of yours? Did he make you
long for the feel of his arms about you, the pressure of his
lips?'

'Stop it, Ricardo,' she said desperately. 'That's not how it
was at all. Like you said, we're both English and inclined
towards informality. Nothing happened between us. All we
did was talk.'

His eyes narrowed. 'About what did you talk?'

'All sorts of things.' Despite all she could do to stop it, her
glance slid away from his. 'About home—about his job.'

'You lie to me.' He was across the room and swinging her
round by the arms to face him before she could move. The
dark eyes were glittering, his mouth a cruel taut line. 'You
talk to him about me—about our marriage, is that not so?'

At that moment he had never been more foreign, even his
accent thickened into unfamiliarity. He shook her, fingers
bruising her flesh. 'Is that not so?'

'No!' She was quivering and unnerved, her own eyes
wide and almost as dark as his against the whiteness of her
face. 'Not—not in the way you mean. He guessed some of it
himself.'

'*Guessed?*' The disbelief seared. 'How could anyone *guess* a situation of this kind!'

'I meant he guessed something wasn't quite right between us and drew his own conclusions.'

'Without even having seen us together? Clever of him. Extremely clever!' The grip on her upper arm did not relax. 'And what were these conclusions he drew?'

Lian took a breath, knowing she was going to have to tell him something and knowing herself incapable at that moment of making anything up. 'He thinks I married you because I felt myself bound to,' she got out. 'I could hardly pretend to be in love with you.'

Ricardo hardly appeared to have heard the last. 'Bound to?' he repeated slowly, then his expression took on sudden enlightenment. 'You mean because I had already possessed you?' The laugh was short and sharp and totally without humour. 'He credits the two of us with codes of conduct I would have thought quite foreign to the English way of life nowadays. A marriage of redemption. On my side conscience, on yours morality.'

'Aren't they the same thing?'

His lips thinned anew. 'Do not try to teach me the nuances of your language. This is neither the time nor the place. If our guest believes us already in knowledge of one another then we had better put truth to the matter, had we not?'

'No!' She tried to jerk free of him, her heart leaping into her throat, but he held her firmly. 'Ricardo, you can't!'

'You think not?' He bent and swung her up in his arms, face taut with intent in the pale light. 'We shall see.'

She fought him as he carried her across to the bed, but made little impression. Flat in the pillows, she looked up into his shadowed features as he knelt above her to strip off his jacket and made one more attempt to reason with him. 'You realise what it will mean if you do—this?'

'If I take you?' he supplied softly. 'If I possess my wife in every last sense of the word? Yes, I know what it will mean. And I have told you it would come to this if you goaded me to it. Also that I will find other means of ending our contract in such a case. There is no way out. You are going to know the man you married as a wife *should* know her husband!'

Lian twisted her head away as he sought her mouth, until he took her chin in his hand and held her still. The kiss was long and slow and searching, his body sinking down to pinion her, his hands laying claim. The fight died out of her as other emotions swathed her heart and her mind. She didn't hate Ricardo; she wasn't sure just what she felt. If this was what he wanted, and there was no way of denying him, then why not let it happen? He was her husband; there was nothing wrong in giving herself to him.

But he didn't love her, she reminded herself forcibly. And without love the act was just a hollow ritual. In responding to him she was condoning a union which could bring neither of them any happiness.

He lifted his head as he sensed the change in her, the fire still leaping in his eyes, breathing ragged. For a long moment he looked down at her, studying her face in the dim light, then with a visible effort he brought himself under control, pressing upwards and away from her.

'You are right,' he said harshly. 'The satisfaction would be short-lived compared with the complications it would bring. I will take my pleasure instead in the knowledge of how close you came to giving yourself willingly to me.' He saw her wince and smiled with mockery. 'The truth is often unpalatable. Should it be any consolation, I do not find it easy to leave you. My senses tell me to take you back in my arms and to the devil with tomorrow. Right now, this moment, I desire you with a fervour difficult to deny. Does that please you?'

Lian moved her head once from side to side on the pillow, throat tight. 'No, it doesn't please me. It isn't *me* you want.'

His gaze went slowly over the length of her, covered only by the soft clinging lines of her nightdress. 'If by that you mean I covet your body rather than your mind, you are possibly right. You are beautiful, *chica*, with that curve of breast and hip which drives a man to distraction even when fully clothed.' He caught her hands as she attempted to pull the folds of her loosened wrap about. 'No! If I wish to tantalise myself with the sight of you then that is my right. If I wish to touch you, to caress you, I shall do this too!' The flame was back in his eyes. 'Perhaps, after all, I cannot bring myself to leave you. I must have you, Lian. I *must*!'

'What about the complications?' she whispered desperately. 'Ricardo——'

'It will be worth it,' he murmured against her skin. 'I will make it worth it—for both of us. Relax, little one. Stop fighting me. Put your arms about me and let me love you.'

She made no move to respond, forcing herself to rigid stillness. 'Don't call it love,' she said with contempt. 'You're no different from your father!'

It was his turn now to be still, his hands holding her in a feather-light caress, his lips at the base of her throat. How long a time passed before he moved, she had no clear idea. It seemed an age; it was probably mere seconds. When he pushed himself away from her she was terrified by the look on his face. She put out a hand to him gropingly, but he brushed it away with a ferocity that wrenched her shoulder, pinning it down by the wrist on the pillow beside her head.

'You will rue the day you ever say that to me again,' he threatened in low rough tones. 'If I were no different from my father you would do so now! Keep your chastity if it means so much to you. I have lost all desire to share your bed!'

It was only after the door had closed behind him that Lian could find the will to sit up, her fingers ruefully circling the bruised wrist. She had won, but at what cost? Ricardo hated her now; she had seen it in his eyes. Yet had she accepted the alternative she would have hated herself.

He had left his suit jacket where he had flung it on the chair at the side of the bed. Involuntarily, she reached out and took it in her hands, smoothing the material, then putting it to her face to smell the familiar aroma of the cheroot he had smoked downstairs. Why had it to be like this? Why couldn't she and Ricardo have met on another plane, where their attraction for one another might have developed into something real? Because they had been attracted, both of them, from the start, no matter how much either might try to deny it.

And since? Could simple attraction make her feel the way she had these last days—the way she still did despite all that had happened here in this room tonight? Ricardo had wanted her and had made her want him in return. He had set her alight, and not just physically. Not love, she pleaded with herself silently. That would be too ironic. He would never forgive her for what she had said, nor would he touch her again. What might just conceivably have been was finished before it had even begun. There was desolation in the knowledge.

Grant was a welcome addition to the household during the days following. Without him Lian didn't think she could have stood the atmosphere prevalent now between her and the man she had married. Not that Ricardo gave any surface sign of his feelings. Only on the rare occasions when they were alone together did he allow the glitter to show in his eyes as he looked at her, the coldness to enter his voice.

Lian had considered bringing the whole thing out in the open by offering her apology for comparing him with his father, except that she didn't know how to phrase it; wasn't even sure why he considered it so damning an insult. There had been no love lost between father and son, that was apparent, but this went deeper than mere animosity. She had hurt Ricardo in a way she would rather hurt no one, no

matter what the provocation. No apology was going to lessen
that hurt; it might even add fuel to the fire. The only thing
she could do was to let it ride, and gain comfort from the
knowledge that she was safe from further emotional strain.

True to his word, Ricardo spent a large part of his time
with his estate managers, leaving her to entertain Grant in
the best way she could. The two of them rode a lot, and
talked about everything under the sun, swapping reminis-
cences, discovering mutual places they knew or had visited.

'You're homesick,' he said once, watching her face as she
described the big old house which had been her home from
the age of three. 'You'll be even more so when I'm gone. At
least we can communicate.'

Lian put up a hand and pushed her hair from her eyes in
a gesture unconsciously defensive. 'My Spanish is improving
by leaps and bounds,' she said lightly. 'It isn't often I'm
caught out these days.'

'That wasn't what I meant, and you know it. The whole
culture is different from ours. I don't see you adapting.'

There was no lasting reason for her to adapt, but he wasn't
to know that.

'It takes time,' she said. 'I've only been here a few weeks.
There's a lot to learn.'

'Like subservience to your own husband, for instance?'
His tone was low and deliberate. 'There's no such thing as
a marriage partnership in this part of the world. You're his
possession. You've no redress against him in law, no matter
how he treats you. Did you know that?'

She lay back on the rug they had spread beside the car
for their picnic, feeling the warmth of the sun on her cheekbones. 'I've never thought about it.'

'Then it's time you did.' He paused for a moment before
going on slowly, 'I can understand you being drawn to him
in the first place. He's the kind of man women seem to find
exciting—sure of himself, powerful——'

'Rich?' she suggested without inflection.

'Stop it!' He was suddenly angry. 'Stop trying to make yourself out to be what you're not! Tell me to mind my own damned business, if you like, but don't take me for a fool!'

'I'm sorry.' She sat up again, reaching out a hand impulsively towards him, to have it taken in a firm grasp. 'I don't take you for a fool, Grant. Far from it. I appreciate your concern, really I do, only——'

'Only?' he prompted as she broke off.

She shook her head. 'It isn't something I can discuss. I'm married to Ricardo and that's that.'

'But you don't love him.' It was a statement, not a question. 'I'm pretty sure of that.'

'It must be nice to be so certain.' She took back her hand and pushed herself to her knees, face closed against him. 'We'd better be going. We're almost on Riga land as it is.'

Grant made no attempt to re-open the subject. 'Why not pay your in-laws a visit?' he suggested. 'Seeing we're so close. I'd like to meet them.'

She looked at him swiftly, to meet his bland regard. She had told him simply that there was little communication between the two families without going into details. 'I don't think so,' she said. 'I explained the situation.'

'A family tiff.' He shook his head. 'These things only get out of hand if everybody contributes. I thought you said you'd like to know your sister-in-law better?'

'Yes, I did.' She was aware of sudden temptation. Why not? Someone had to take the first steps towards breaking down the barriers, even if it were only between her and Isabella. The Argentinian girl had shown distinct leanings in that direction herself on the one disastrous occasion they had met.

'All right,' she said before she could change her mind. 'We'll go. Only don't be surprised if Carlos greets us with some animosity, if he's around.'

'Can't see why he should if it's Ricardo he had the row with.' Picking up and shaking the rug, Grant added, 'I can't quite see Ricardo himself being so petty-minded as to keep something like this on for any length of time. Must have been a fair disagreement. To do with the *estancia*, I expect. Doesn't Carlos own any of it?'

'Ricardo was willing to share with him.' Lian registered the defensive note in her voice with surprise.

'Providing he remained in full control, of course.'

'Well, yes. Mendoza is legally his.' She watched him get behind the wheel before saying softly, 'You don't like Ricardo very much any more, do you, Grant?'

'I can't fathom him out,' he admitted after a moment. 'He isn't the same man I met in Rio.'

'Not in any way?'

'Not in many ways. He had more warmth about him, from what I can remember. We got quite pally those few days, which is more than can be said for now.' He swung his head to look at her. 'I wondered if he might object to the amount of time we've been spending together.'

'If he did he'd say so,' Lian responded. 'It could be just that you're expecting too much of a few days' acquaintance. Everyone is different when they're on holiday.'

'More relaxed, maybe, not fundamentally.'

She forced a smile. 'Do you analyse everybody you meet this way?'

'Meaning it's unusual for my type to look any further than the end of their nose?' His shrug was without resentment. 'There's a lot of spare time in my line of work, and often enough nowhere to spend it. I've studied a bit of psychology, enough to recognise basic traits. It didn't take any trained eye to see you were under strain when we first met. It was right there in your face. It still is.'

'Don't they say the first year of any marriage is the worst?'

'Don't joke about it,' he said. 'You'll not convince me it's nothing more than normal adjustment. The situation isn't normal.'

By how far she hoped he would never know. 'We must go,'

she said, 'or there isn't going to be time to get there and back before dark. It's still quite a distance to the *casa* itself.'

'All right,' he said wryly, 'so you can't bring yourself to trust me yet. There's a lot more to this marriage of yours than you're letting on, and we both know it. Just promise me one thing. If you're ever in need of any help you can reach me through the company office in B.A. Will do?'

'You haven't even gone yet,' she protested, and knew a swift sense of distress at the very thought of his leaving. 'I promise,' she said, striving for a light note. 'We British must stick together!'

'Always,' he came back with the subtle emphasis, and started the engine with a brisk flick of his wrist.

CHAPTER SEVEN

THEY came into view of the Riga *casa* just after three. It was the first time Lian had seen the place in daylight, and she found herself warming to its weathered stone and uneven lines. Not as magnificent as Mendoza but friendlier by half. If she had to live in this place she could have wished for a house like this one.

As was usual during *siesta* time, there was no one about. It was probably the wrong time to come visiting, but now they were here they could hardly turn about without announcing their presence. A servant came out through the archway from the courtyard as Grant brought the car to a halt, hastily buttoning a clean white shirt.

'Señora Mendoza and Señor Edwards to see Señora Mendoza,' Lian told him, feeling uncomfortable and uncertain now that they were actually on the doorstep, so to speak.

From the expression on his face, the servant shared her uncertainty. The Señora was resting through in the courtyard, he told them. They would come this way.

Isabella laid down the book she had been reading as the little party appeared in her vision, her expression passing through wide-eyed surprise to sudden, heart-warming pleasure.

'You have come, as I hoped you would!' she exclaimed, rising to her feet to greet them. The vivid face was alive and smiling. 'I thought that Ricardo would never allow it. He is with you?'

Lian shook her head, aware that she must invite Isabella into a mutual deception for the time being. 'He doesn't know we're here at all, or he certainly wouldn't have allowed it. This is Grant Edwards who is staying at Mendoza with us. Grant is an oil man working in the Chaco at present.'

'For our country or for your own?' Isabella asked with some interest, and he grinned.

'For yours. I'm only lending a hand.'

'But an expert one, I am sure.' She waved a hand towards the chairs placed within the shade of the inner walls. 'Let us sit down and I will have drinks fetched. Carlos is changing his clothing. He will be joining us in a few moments.' She caught Lian's change of expression and smiled. 'You must not be wary of Carlos. He will be pleased that you do not share Ricardo's mistrust. Men are so intense in their feeling, do you not find? There is no give and take.'

'Personally,' Grant said, 'I find women the worst kind of enemies. But that's only the opinion of a mere male.'

His hostess wrinkled her nose at him, returning his laugh. 'You tease me because I generalise. I should not do it, I agree, but the temptation is often strong. You are here for long, Señor Edwards?'

'Perhaps another week,' he said. 'And the name is Grant.'

She inclined her lovely dark head with a wicked little glint in her eyes. 'I will call you Grant when Carlos is not present. He would not much like such swift familiarity. Lian, my sister, how do you find La Pampa now that you have been here a little time? Do the space and emptiness bore you as they do most Europeans?'

'I felt a bit lost at first,' Lian confessed. 'I was frightened of getting lost with so few landmarks to find my way back by, until I realised that my horse would always find his way home.'

'You ride? That is good! The motor vehicle is excellent for reaching one's destination quickly, but not as pleasurable as a good horse. Ricardo has given you one of your own?'

'More or less. He's a gelding called Rojo.'

'I know the animal. A safe, solid mount, though not too exciting. Ricardo is mean; he keeps the best of his domestic string for himself.' Her eyes were sparkling with mischief. 'He does not know it, but I once rode Diablo myself when he was away. It was not easy, and Carlos was furious when he came upon us, although he promised to say nothing to Ricardo when I pleaded with him.'

Grant was listening with an odd expression in his eyes. 'That was before they fell out?'

'*Si.*' Isabella looked sad. 'Though they have never been the friends brothers should be. Since I married Carlos I have seen Ricardo only once, and that was not a pleasant occasion.' She brightened as the figure of her husband appeared from within the house. 'Carlos, see who has come to visit us! Is it not good?'

The handsome, dark-skinned face was hard to read as he came forward to where they sat. He was wearing casual slacks and shirt, and looked rather less impressive than he had the night of his wedding. His smile, when it came, was not wholly without restraint.

'It is good, if unexpected,' he agreed. 'Ricardo does not know you are here?'

Lian shook her head, regretting the apparent disloyalty of her action. By being here at all she was as good as stating her sympathies. She introduced Grant, and watched the two men weigh one another up as they shook hands European fashion. There was something a little disquieting in the Argentinian's expression when he moved away to take a seat.

'You have much longer to work in the Chaco?' he inquired.

'Depends on when we strike, if ever. We were down to twelve hundred when I left. If it's there we should find it around twenty-six hundred.'

'And if this well is dry you will try again elsewhere?'

'That's the general idea. According to the geologists it's down there somewhere. All we have to do is find the right spot, or spots.'

'Like looking for your proverbial needle in the haystack, perhaps?'

'Not quite as bad as that. At least we have some idea where to start looking.'

Isabella got to her feet. 'You would like perhaps to see the rest of our home while the men talk?' she asked Lian. 'It is cooler indoors.'

Lian agreed with a reluctance she was unable to account for. She didn't want to leave the two men together, yet what was she afraid of? The worst Carlos could do was to suggest that her own marriage had been deliberately timed to take Mendoza away from him, but even he didn't know the full extent of the plot. More than likely he wouldn't even mention the matter. Why should he? Grant was in no way involved in the affairs of the Mendozas.

The *casa* was as comfortable inside as its outward appearance suggested, the floors mainly tiled, with scattered rugs and skins to take away the bareness. Isabella apologised that her parents were not available to meet her.

'They grow old and need their rest,' she said. '*Siesta* is still taken seriously by those of their generation as a time for sleep. Only as the weather grows cooler will they begin to change their habits. Carlos does not return home at all until nightfall in the winter when he is out with the *gauchos*. There is much to do at that time of the year.'

'I gathered you used to spend quite a lot of time at Mendoza in the past?' Lian said with casual interest as they progressed through the *casa*.

'Oh yes.' The other girl laughed. 'There was a time, I must confess, when I imagined myself in love with Ricardo.'

'Until Carlos came along?'

'Oh, and after that too. It was not until the day he saved me from being thrown by Diablo that I realised he was the one I truly wanted. A woman has to be needed as well as loved, as you will know yourself.'

Well, she had certainly been needed, Lian acknowledged

dryly, trying to ignore the dull ache in her chest. One might even say Ricardo had been desperate for her. She thought of how he must have felt seeing the girl he loved betrothed to the brother he despised, and knew a swift pang of compassion. Small wonder his deeper emotions were held under such tight rein. Never again would a woman hurt him that way.

Carlos and Grant were still sitting where they had left them when they returned to the courtyard. She thought the latter looked at her a little strangely, but he sounded normal enough when he suggested it might be time to go.

They took their leave under many injunctions from Isabella to come again before Grant's visit was over.

'She's a dish,' he commented approvingly when they were clear of the homestead. 'I can see why you'd like her. There's no bitchiness in either of you.'

Lian laughed. 'Why should there be?'

'Because you're both good-looking, and two equally attractive women don't usually hit it off so well—it's against nature.'

'You're a cynic,' she came back tolerantly.

'I'm a realist,' he corrected. 'Who was it said, when women kiss it's like prizefighters shaking hands?'

'I can't imagine. It sounds like something out of the *Reader's Digest*.'

'It probably is. I've got a whole stack of them back at camp.' He glanced her way for a moment, eyes assessing. 'Glad I persuaded you to go?'

'Yes and no.' She looked back at him, lifted her shoulders in a wry little gesture. 'I feel disloyal to Ricardo. He'll be furious when he knows.'

'Then don't tell him.'

'If I don't I'm almost sure Carlos will have him informed.'

'Oh, I don't know. Struck me as a decent enough character taken all round. You didn't tell me he was only Ricardo's half-brother.'

'Obviously *he* did.' She paused before adding casually, 'What else did you two talk about?'

'Oh, this and that.' There was evasion in the airy reply. 'These dirt roads are more monotonous than the motorways back home. Give me a bit of changing scenery any day. Even the Chaco has contrast.'

Lian said, 'I read somewhere that the Chaco region was often flooded.'

'The lowlands are. I'm talking about the extreme north-west, up towards Salta. Nobody out there except Indians and a few settlers.'

Lian went on listening with only half an ear. Carlos had told Grant something; his swift change of subject confirmed that. But how much? The whole story or just enough of it to elicit his sympathies? The latter seemed more likely. Carlos needed to discredit Ricardo, not lay bare the details of their relationship: the brother deprived of his rightful inheritance by last-minute trickery; that would probably be the line he would have taken.

They had covered some three miles when they saw the small cloud of dust approaching from the other direction. Shortly it resolved itself into a wagon and team with an accompanying rider. Lian felt her heart sink as she recognised the unmistakable size and colour of the latter's mount.

'It's Ricardo,' she said. 'You'd better slow down, Grant.'

The wagon was driven by one of the Mendoza hands. As he reined in the team opposite the halted car, they saw the sprawled carcases of several sheep in the back of the wagon, heads lolling in death. Ricardo brought the big black up close to where Grant sat at the wheel, his face hard and grim.

'Where have you been?' he demanded.

It was Lian who answered, striving to keep her tone matter-of-fact. 'To see Isabella.'

His hands tightened on the reins, bringing the stallion's head jerking upwards. 'We will discuss this later,' he said.

To Grant he added harshly, 'You will please return my wife home at once.'

The other man made a placatory gesture. 'Look, it was my fault we went to the Riga place. I asked Lian to take me. Sorry if I stepped out of line, but don't lay the blame at her door.'

The lean features did not relax. 'I will decide at whose door to lay the blame, as you so succinctly put it. Go now.'

'Ricardo.' Lian was gazing at the wagon, her throat dry and aching. 'Did you shoot those sheep yourself?'

'They were shot on my orders,' he said. 'The responsibility is mine. You will not concern yourself with such matters.'

He clipped an order to the man driving the wagon, and urged Diablo into motion as the wheels began to turn. Grant gave a wry grimace and let in the clutch, coughing a little as dust from the receding vehicle swirled in through the opened window.

'Seems we got caught at a bad time,' he said. 'What was all that about the sheep?'

Numbly, she said, 'Ricardo threatened Carlos he would do it if he found them on Mendoza land again. He believes Carlos is driving them in deliberately to break his taboos.'

'Is it so important to him not to have sheep on his land?'

'Apparently it's everything to him. An affair of principle. Sheep and cattle should never be mixed on the same land.'

'Plenty of other *estancieros* do it without apparent harmful effects.'

'I don't think his aversion has anything to do with the actual harm they might do to the alfalfa, just the basic idea.'

'Allowed to grow until it takes over from reason,' Grant murmured thoughtfully. 'Like this feud he has with his brother.'

'Half-brother,' she corrected without thinking about it, then broke off and caught at her lip. Now she was doing it too! 'There's rather more to it than I think you understand,' she added on a subdued note.

'So tell me about it.'

'I can't.'

'Loyalty?' he suggested. The pause stretched, then he said on an altered note, 'Lian, I don't know what hold he has over you, but I'm pretty sure you were forced into marrying him.'

She kept her eyes front. 'Because of what Carlos told you?' she asked painfully.

'If you like. It was too quick, too convenient. Do you deny it?'

'Yes,' she said. 'I was given a choice. Don't ask me any more, Grant, because I won't discuss it with you. It isn't my problem to discuss.'

'It has to be your problem if it affects you in any way. And it does—in every way. You can't live the rest of your life to Ricardo's will and whim. Even if you loved him——'

'What makes you so sure I don't?' she flashed, driven by some emotion beyond her control, and something altered in his expression.

'Do you?' he asked after a long moment.

Her adrenalin level sank as quickly as it had risen. 'I don't know,' she admitted helplessly. 'I just don't know what I feel.'

'Then it isn't love, whatever it is.' He was watching the dusty track ahead, tension in the line of his mouth. 'Can I ask you a personal question?'

'No,' she said, knowing what was coming. 'No, you can't. Please, don't get involved, Grant.'

'I'm already involved.' It was so quietly said she barely heard him. 'I was involved the moment we met. And I'm not going to leave it like this. I can't. Not unless and until you can convince me you want to stay with Ricardo.'

She gazed at him on a sudden surge of conflicting emotions, tempted once more to blurt. out the truth. Yet what good would it do? The marriage was valid if not intended to last, and Ricardo was hardly going to let her break their bargain.

Their bargain? *His*, didn't she mean? He had been the one to set a price on her agreement, and force her into acceptance. She hadn't wanted the money then, and she didn't want it now.

They barely spoke again till reaching Mendoza. Lian slipped out of the car with a murmured word of excuse and almost ran indoors. What time Ricardo would return she had no idea. Darkness would be upon them in less than half an hour. Lying in the bath, she thought again of the hardness in his face when he had come upon them, of the pathetic bodies in the wagon. What kind of a man was it who would put a bullet in an animal just for the sake of a principle? He could so easily have driven the sheep back and repaired the fencing. Carlos would soon have tired of the game if he had seen no apparent effect.

She heard his voice down in the courtyard while she was dressing, the accents clipped as if anger still lurked. From the speed of his return, there could have been little time lost in discussion with his brother. Lian could imagine him tipping the carcases to the ground in front of Carlos, imagine too the burning glance he would have cast in Isabella's direction had she been present. She was the one most of this was about, yet the fault was hardly hers. Ricardo must realise she had had a right to her choice.

This time he knocked and waited for an invitation before entering her room. He looked tired, she thought; a weariness born of something deeper than mere physical exertion. He didn't speak for a moment, eyes slightly narrowed as he regarded her.

'Do you take pleasure in defying my wishes?' he asked at last.

'No,' she answered levelly.

'You hoped, perhaps, that I would not know of your visit to the Riga Estancia?'

'No,' she said again. 'As a matter of fact, I was sure you would find out.'

His brows rose. 'So you have no fear of my anger?'

'Is that what you want?' she demanded, swinging right round on the dressing chest stool to face him. Her heart was beating fast but her chin was held high. 'For me to fear you! Is that the only way you know to gain compliance?' She pressed herself unsteadily to her feet, aware of her disadvantage in continuing to sit. 'I wanted to see Isabella. She's the only other female round here I can really talk to. Is that so hard to understand?'

'You saw Carlos too,' he said, ignoring the latter question. 'He took great pleasure in flinging the fact in my face!'

'As you no doubt took pleasure in flinging *his* sheep at his feet!'

'Riga sheep. And he was warned.' He held up a hand as she made to speak. 'I will listen to no more. You not only defy me, you stay out almost the whole of the day with our guest!'

'I thought you wanted him entertained.'

'Not in so flagrant a fashion. Do you think the servants have not noted how you laugh and talk together—how you use any excuse to be close to one another!'

'That isn't true!'

'No?' The inflection was deadly. 'It has been remarked upon.'

'By Inez, I suppose?'

'By whom is of no matter. I intend to stand no more of it. Unless you wish your countryman's visit to be cut short you will begin to use circumspection in your dealings with him.' The level, measured delivery emphasised the words more effectively than any raised tones. 'As to the other matter——' the pause was brief but calculated—'if there is a next time you will be sorry, I promise you that. You will stay away from the Riga Estancia!'

Lian sat gazing at the door for several moments after he had gone, heart heavy. There was no getting through to him at all. He was as hard as iron, and twice as unyielding. She

recalled the days prior to Grant's arrival; before the night he
had come here to her room. There had been times then when
she had felt close to understanding him, but those days were
past. There was nothing but enmity between them now, and
still five months of their agreement to go. Could she stand
it so long? Yet what was the alternative? She had no way of
getting home if she left Mendoza—not even of getting to the
coast. And she would still be married to Ricardo if she made
her escape. There was no way out.

She was subdued at dinner, conscious of the dark, sardonic
eyes at the head of the table, and of concerned lighter ones
as Grant kept glancing her way. Whether anything had been
said to the latter regarding his part in the afternoon's events,
she had no way of knowing, although there was no apparent
difference in the attitude of the two men towards one another.

Afterwards, she accepted a brandy to go with her coffee,
needing the stimulation. The night was clouded, the air
unusually heavy, with a fitful wind from the north-east doing
little to stir it.

'Tomorrow there will be a storm,' Ricardo asserted. He
didn't glance in Lian's direction as he added in the same level
tone, 'I would have suggested that you both of you accompany me on a flight down to Tandil in the morning, but under
the circumstances I think you might be more comfortable here
at Mendoza. I shall be back before nightfall.'

'Will flying be safe at all if there's to be a storm?' Grant
inquired into the momentary silence, and received a shrug
in reply.

'I hope I shall not be caught in it. The journey is essential
or I would not be making it at such a time.'

He wasn't referring just to the storm, Lian knew. He didn't
trust the two of them alone together. Anger mingled with
pain, the former strengthening to swamp the latter as if with
purpose. Who was he to judge anyone else's moral values?
He used people; he deserved no better than to be used in
return. Grant was worth two of him!

She saw his departure next morning in the same state of self-protective hatred, turning back to Grant with a smile which ignored the silent, watchful presence of the housekeeper on the staircase behind him.

'If we're going to get our ride today we'd better take it now before the rain comes, don't you think? Ricardo is never wrong about the weather.'

If he was surprised by her mood he didn't show it. 'Okay,' he said easily. 'I'm game. How about taking a run into Santina this afternoon if it holds off?'

'Why not?' At that precise moment Lian would have agreed to go anywhere so long as it was away from Mendoza. 'Let's make a real day of it!'

Ricardo had apparently left no instructions against their riding together, for the horses were saddled without demur at her request.

'The rain come soon,' advised the elderly stable hand Lian knew only as Pedro, indicating the massing clouds. 'Big storm!'

'We'll be back before it breaks,' she assured him, and wheeled Rojo into a canter out of the stable forecourt with a feeling that if they didn't go now they never would at all.

Grant caught up with her on the big bay which had been his own choice of mount this morning, his sideways glance assessing. 'Where's the fire?'

She slowed the gelding with reluctance, bringing him down to a walk. 'Sorry, I just felt like it.'

'Breaking out, you mean?' He gave her no time to reply, if there was a reply. 'Gestures won't help. Decisions are what you need.'

'Don't.' Her voice sounded thick and heavy. 'We're not starting that again, Grant.'

'All right,' he said. 'You're the boss. How about a race? Bet I can beat you to the next windpump!'

They made it neck to neck, both horses stretched though not winded. Laughing, they reined in to let the animals rest, the steam rising from damp hides pungent on the air. Above them the pump sails turned woodenly, splashing water into the trough alongside. Cattle grazed nearby, pulling at the blue forage plant covering the plain. The Sierra looked one with the cloud piled beyond it, the familiar serrated line blurred and indistinct. Somewhere to the west lay Tandil.

'Feeling better?' Grant asked softly, and she gave a faint wry smile.

'You don't let up, do you?'

'Not in this particular case.' His tone was level, with an underlying depth. 'I happen to have a vested interest.'

She looked at him quickly and away again, pulse jerking. 'We ought to be moving on. That rain is going to come heavy when it does come.'

'So what?' he said. 'We can only get wet. Let's ride out to the railhead and back.'

'Why the railhead?'

He shrugged. 'It's somewhere to go. There aren't all that many places out here.'

It's too far, she started to say, then stopped and let it pass. As he said, what did it matter? They could get wet.

They took their time on the way out, walking the horses side by side so that they could talk. Once they saw a small group of Mendoza *gauchos* riding towards the house. Greetings were exchanged, and Lian was aware of dark inquisitive glances directed her way. Word would reach Ricardo of this latest indiscretion, but she told herself she didn't care. There was nothing wrong in riding out alone with a guest of the household. Let him do his worst!

Apart from the cattle pens, there was little in the way of creature comfort about the Mendoza rail halt. In the remote chance of anyone wishing to alight from the one passenger train which used this branch line per day, there was a waiting room of sorts, consisting of a tin-roofed hut some ten feet by six with a couple of bench seats on the bare wooden floor. The threatened rain came in a sudden solid deluge when they were still some distance away from the line itself, soaking them both to the skin in seconds as they raced for cover.

The lean-to next to the hut provided shelter for the horses. With girths loosened, the latter seemed content enough to be left while their human partners sought better protection within the hut itself.

'Not that it's going to make much difference now,' Lian acknowledged with wry laughter, viewing her sodden clothing. 'Good thing it's still warm. A good gallop back when it stops and they'll probably dry on us.'

'*When* it stops,' Grant said from the doorway as thunder rolled in the distance. 'If that's coming this way we might be stuck out here for hours.'

'In which case we'll just have to ride through it,' she responded at once, and he turned to look at her.

'Scared of what might happen if Ricardo gets back before we do?'

She refused to meet his eyes. 'Ricardo will be in Tandil by now. If this keeps up he might not get back at all.'

'I think he will, if only to make sure we're behaving ourselves,' with a twisted grin. 'He doesn't trust me with you.'

'You're wrong,' she said without emotion. 'It's me he doesn't trust. He thinks I encourage familiarity.'

'So you do, in the nicest possible way.' He hadn't moved from where he stood, but there was something in his stance that triggered her senses. 'It's like calling to like—we gravitate together. If we'd met before you got into this marriage it would have been the same.'

Lian stared at him, wondering if that were strictly true. Circumstances had thrown them together and aroused his interest. Had they been different she would have been just another girl. A man like Grant needed challenge, she realised. Danger too, for preference. In this situation he could find both.

'Just what did Carlos tell you?' she said.

'Enough to make me realise you were being used.' He paused before adding, 'Did you know before you married him why Ricardo wanted a wife so quickly?'

'Yes,' she said, 'I knew.'

'Yet you still went ahead.'

'Obviously.' She saw his indrawn lip and made a gesture of appeasement. 'Grant, please let's leave it alone. There's no amount of talking about it going to change things. It's done and I'm stuck with it.'

Something altered in his expression. 'You don't have to be stuck with it. I can take you out of it—if you'll let me.'

The silence stretched between them for an age, broken only by the sound of the rain hammering against the tin roof and the distant rolling of thunder. When Lian did speak it was in a voice which sounded totally unlike her own.

'I know you're trying to be kind and thoughtful,' she said, 'but it's no solution. You have a job to go to, and I don't have any money of my own. Neither,' she added quickly, seeing his mouth open, 'would I consider borrowing from you to get me back to England. It's sweet of you to be concerned, and I'll always be grateful——'

'Lian!' He came away from the doorpost, reaching for her with determined hands. 'I'm not just trying to be kind, you little fool! I want you out of this mess for my sake as much as yours. What do I have to say to get through to you how I feel?' Looking down into the darkened green eyes, his own kindled into fresh resolve. 'Oh, to hell with talking round it!'

Lian made no move to avoid his lips, aware of confusion as his arms tightened about her. She had known Grant was attracted to her, but this was something more; something deeper. Emotion stirred within her in response, pressing her involuntarily closer to him, sliding her arms up and about his neck, seeking reassurance in the very quality of his need. When they finally drew apart it was with reluctance on both sides. Lian was trembling, heart full and aching. This was what it *should* be like.

'That was more than I had any right to hope for,' he said very softly. 'I knew we had a lot going for us, but you've been so close about your own feelings this last week.' He paused, voice gruffening a little. 'I love you, Lian. I guess I went overboard that first night. You've got to let me take you away from here. We can sort things out. Ricardo has no moral right to you.'

'He has legal rights,' she said in the grip of painful reality. 'I can't leave Mendoza, Grant. He won't let me go.'

'We won't ask him.' There was sudden decision in his tone. 'We'll go now—today—before he gets back. I can charter a plane from Santina. Once we get to B.A. he's going to find it a damned sight harder to enforce any kind of rights!'

Her face was pale and drawn, eyes widened. 'Grant, it's impossible! You know it is!'

'I don't know anything of the sort. Nothing's impossible if we both want it hard enough.' He was urgent and persuasive. 'We can be back at the house within an hour if we ride through this lot. Another hour to change and throw a few things together, and maybe a couple more to reach Santina. Ricardo won't be back before tonight, if he makes it at all. By that time we'll be in B.A.'

'The staff,' she said wildly. 'What about the staff?'

'What about them? They can't stop us leaving. Just let 'em try!' He caught her up again, kissing her with a passion that spoke already of possessiveness, feverish in his need to convince her. 'You're coming with me, sweetheart. You want to come with me. You *know* you want to come with me, don't you?'

In his arms, Lian couldn't think straight at all. She didn't love Grant, yet he made her feel safe and secure and wanted —not just as Ricardo wanted her, but in the way a woman longed for. There would be nothing easy about this thing he was asking her to do. He would be letting himself in for trouble of a kind most men would run from. Yet he obviously deemed it worth it if it meant he could have her. Such a man would be easy to fall in love with because she *wanted* to love him. Together they could face anything Ricardo tried to do.

'All right,' she said thickly, 'I'll go with you, Grant. Only let's hurry. Please let's hurry!'

CHAPTER EIGHT

AFTERWARDS she remembered little of that ride back through the teeming rain, except for feeling sorry for the horses forced to forge a path over sodden *pampas* which would be dry again only a short time after the rain stopped. Pedro greeted them with an air of self-justification, despatching both animals for a rub-down by two of the boys under his command in obvious disgust at their state.

They went into the house the back way through the courtyard and up the outer staircase to the balcony without seeing or being seen by anyone. At the top, Grant said swiftly:

'I'll get my things and come along to your room. Can you manage?'

'I don't have a suitcase,' she admitted, recalling its disappearance. A strange kind of acceptance seemed to have settled on her. 'I'll put a few things in with yours and make do with what I stand up in.'

'We can buy whatever you need later,' he agreed. He put a hand behind her head and drew her to him to press his lips swiftly to hers once more. 'I won't be long.'

She was changed into a linen trouser suit when he did come into her room through the open balcony doors, her hair swept up to conceal damp ends and half hidden beneath a toning beige and tan scarf. He was wearing the same safari-styled suit in which he had arrived and carried a brown leather suitcase which proved only two thirds full. It took only moments to fold the items she had put ready in on top of his own things. She did it automatically, not trying to think. Grant was in charge; she would simply go along. It was

better this way; better and easier. She didn't want to have to
think—about anything.

Inez was crossing the hall when they descended the stairs
together. She stopped in her tracks to stare at them, eyes
taking in the evidence of the suitcase without at first appearing to register the meaning.

'We are leaving,' Grant said in Spanish. 'You can tell your
master we won't be coming back.'

Lian saw the shocked dismay spring in the dark old eyes
and felt a stirring of sympathy beneath the schooled numb-
ness. To Inez would fall the task of meeting Ricardo with
the news of his wife's departure with their guest. She didn't
envy her the moment.

The car Grant had driven here from the airfield nine days
ago was ready and waiting, with enough in the tank to see
them through the forty miles or so they had to cover. Lian
slid into her seat like an automaton and sat there motion-
lessly while Grant went round to stow the suitcase in the
boot. Then he was getting into the car beside her and switch-
ing on the engine, moving the car forward towards the stone
archway. It was still raining, though with only a fraction of
its former force. The main area of the storm appeared to
have passed to the west. She made no attempt to look back
at the *casa* as they left it behind.

They said little during the long run along roads no longer
dry and dusty, each aware of tension in the other and unwilling to acknowledge it in speech. As each mile fell behind
them, so did Lian's control over her emotions slowly dis-
integrate, try as she might to hang on to the welcome
vacuum. By the time they reached the outskirts of the town
she was shaking inside and feeling almost physically sick.
What was she doing here with Grant like this? How on
earth could they stand a chance of finding happiness together
by running away? If Grant really thought as much of her
as he said he did he would have stayed and faced Ricardo
out, told him he intended taking her away.

Yet was that really fair? Ricardo wouldn't have allowed him to take her away. Not when his control of Mendoza depended upon her staying. He would have had him seen off the *estancia* by his men, probably made sure he was put on a train for the coast. He might even have had him taught a lesson first in order to drive the message home. She pulled herself up there in quick shame. No, that wasn't likely. Any retaliation at all would have come from Ricardo himself at first hand. He wasn't the kind to let others do the dirty work for him. And what about her? She would have had to face the music too. It wasn't a case of which was the best way. This was the *only* way, if she went at all.

The airfield was to the east of the town, consisting of a couple of large hangars and some smaller, tin-roofed buildings, with a cross section of runway laid in concrete. Grant left her sitting in the car outside one of the office buildings while he went to see about transport. He looked far from happy when he came back.

'Nothing for at least a couple of hours,' he said. 'There's only one plane available for charter, and no pilot until they can find him in town.'

'What if he's the worse for drink when they do find him?' Lian ventured.

'I already thought of that.' There was a pause and a change of tone before he added, 'It leaves us with two alternatives. We can either fill up with gas and make for the coast by road, or stay on here in Santina till morning. There's a train running through at six-thirty. Once we're on that we're home and dry.'

Lian's throat had gone dry. 'If we stay here tonight there's every chance Ricardo will find us first.'

'If he gets back to Mendoza at all.' The pause this time was longer. He didn't look at her. 'There's one way we could make sure he won't be taking you back with him if he does come after us.'

'How?'

'By letting him find us together. Latins have a lot of pride. He'd probably refuse to take you back if he thought we were already lovers.'

She said softly, 'He'd probably kill us both.'

'Why should he even try? In marrying him at all you gave him what he needed. There's no reason now for him to be dog-in-the-manger about you.'

'You just mentioned Latin pride. That would be reason enough.' She forced herself to turn her head towards him and voice the doubt creeping into her. 'Grant, are you sure you feel the way you say you do about me? If all you really want is to spend a night with me——'

'It isn't like that!' His hands reached for hers, pulling her towards him, his tone sharp with denial. 'What do you think I am? Of course I want you, but not just for a night. I want to marry you!'

She tried to smile, to believe him. 'What about your six-year plan?'

'To hell with my six-year plan! I hadn't met you when I made it. To hell with this Chaco job too. I'm not going back. They can find somebody else.'

'You can't throw up your whole career,' she protested. 'I won't let you do that for me.'

'You won't stop me. Anyway, I wouldn't be throwing it up altogether, just this job. I can easily get another.'

With a black mark against his name for unreliability. For the first time Lian began to see the possible long-term effects of what they were planning. Her life was already in ruins, but Grant had everything to lose. Whatever he felt for her now, there would surely come a time when it would start to matter that she had been the cause of his downslide; a time when he would start to hate her for putting temptation his way. It wasn't even as though she was in love with him herself; she only hoped to be. If he were going to ruin his career at all it had to be for a more worthy cause.

Slowly she withdrew her hands from his, seeing his face

change with a sickening deadness inside her. 'It won't work,' she said. 'This whole thing is crazy. I'm going back, Grant.'

'No!'

'Yes. I have to.' It took a lot of saying, but it had to be said. 'I was using you as a means of getting out of a situation I wouldn't be in if I'd had more sense. I don't love you. I don't think I ever could.'

'I don't believe that,' he said sturdily. 'You're saying it because you think I'm going to be making sacrifices if I take you with me. You couldn't have kissed me the way you did if you didn't feel something for me.'

'I'm not saying I don't feel *anything* for you,' she came back desperately. 'I like you a whole lot, and I'm attracted to you. When you kissed me this morning I couldn't help kissing you back. You made me feel—needed.'

The brown eyes were hurt. 'And what does Ricardo make you feel? Does his lovemaking compensate for everything else? Is *that* what you don't want to leave?'

Her head jerked as if he had hit her. 'Ricardo doesn't make love to me,' she got out. 'Ours is a business arrangement. In five more months I'll be free to leave Mendoza anyway, so you see there's no need for all this. I'm sorry for misleading you, Grant. I never intended for things to go this far.'

He was staring at her as if he'd never seen her before. 'How do you mean?' he demanded at last. 'What *kind* of business arrangement?'

'I mean that he's paying me to live with him for six months so that he fulfils the terms of his father's will. It isn't turning out to be quite so easy a job as I first anticipated, and that's why I allowed myself to be persuaded to come away with you. Only if I do leave now I stand to lose a small fortune.'

The shake of his head was forceful. 'I don't accept that either,' he said. 'I don't give a damn why you married him, I only know you're desperate to get away from him, and no amount of money would keep you with him if you were able to leave without dragging me in on it.' He reached out and touched her face gently. 'Lian, I was never more glad to hear anything than what you've just told me. I thought you were living with Ricardo in every sense, even though you don't love him—I suppose I just couldn't see a man of his kind leaving you alone. I know I wouldn't have been able to under similar circumstances.'

Her smile was bitter. 'You're never likely to have to put yourself to the test.'

'I hope not.' He was silent for a moment studying her, an odd expression in his eyes. 'Is it because I've made it so obvious that I want you physically as well that you've gone off the idea of coming with me?'

She shook her head wryly. 'Analysis again?'

'An attempt at it. You're not an easy person to understand, and some women do feel that way about so-called male appetites. Love has to be pure and all that!'

'Don't sneer,' she said softly. 'Women just have a different way of seeing things, that's all. Most of us need to be loved without feeling bound to make suitable payment, but given that assurance I daresay we're just as physical in our appetites.'

'So what do you want me to say?'

'Nothing. There's nothing you can say. It wouldn't be fair for me to come with you knowing I'm not in love with you. I have to go back because I'm honour bound to finish what I started.'

He looked at her helplessly. 'How do you think Ricardo is going to react when he hears what happened from Inez? You'll never convince him she made a mistake.'

'I shan't try. Providing I do go back he has no cause to protest too much.'

'I'm not giving up this easily,' he said with a sudden renewal of determination. 'I can't. I don't blame you for not believing how I feel about you. I deserve it for making that suggestion about letting him find us together. We're going to go into town and find a place to stay overnight——' he held up a rueful hand at her quick look—'all right, *places*.

Then we're going to talk our way round this whole damned mess over a good hot meal. You realise we missed lunch?'

Her laugh held a faint quality of hysteria. 'So we did!'

He had to laugh too. 'There's something to be said for getting one's priorities in the right order. We have to be rational about things, Lian.'

It was true, and she knew it. Yet what did rationality have to do with this whole situation? She knew a sudden almost frantic desire to be back at Mendoza with none of this happening. She might be unhappy there, but at least she knew the worst of it.

'Grant, let me take the car and go on back,' she begged. 'You can take the train in the morning.'

'Not without you.' He started the engine and reversed to turn, jaw set stubbornly.

They found a hotel just off the town's central square and Grant booked two rooms. If the desk clerk noticed her lack of personal luggage he made no comment on it. Grant brought in her things, standing a little awkwardly in the doorway while she took them from him.

'I'm going to check on that train time,' he said. 'When would you like to eat?'

She made a small, indecisive gesture. 'I'm not hungry.'

'All right, we'll make it later. I'll call for you at eight. Try and get some rest.'

The solitary window overlooked the street. She went to it, pushing it wide to admit a breath of air freshened by the rain. The skies were clearing, the roadway below already dry. She could see the bell tower of the church in the square, sparkling white against the darkening blue, hear the sound of traffic from the main thoroughfare.

Would Ricardo be home yet, or had he elected to spend the night in Tandil? she wondered. She imagined his reaction on finding her gone and felt a tremor run through her. They were tempting providence by staying here in Santina. They should have taken the car and kept on driving until they were beyond his reach. Yet was that what she really wanted? Once she took that final step he had lost Mendoza. Could she stand to have that on her conscience for the rest of her life?

She was lying on the narrow bed when the knock came on the outer door. Peering at her watch in the darkness of the room, she saw it was only a quarter to eight. Grant was early. She got to her feet and went to open it without bothering to switch on the overhead light, looking into Ricardo's grimly set features in total lack of any kind of feeling at all.

'Put on your shoes,' he said. 'I have a car outside.'

She didn't move. 'Where is Grant?'

Fire blazed in the dark eyes. 'You dare to mention his name to me! He is no longer your concern.'

'Ricardo, please!' Her face was white. 'What have you done to him?'

'I have done nothing to him.' There was self-directed contempt in the denial. 'He will be put unharmed upon the train for the coast in the morning and warned never to return.'

'And if he does?'

'I will kill him.' It was a statement of fact, made all the more convincing by the lack of emotion. 'I will have the right.' The pause was brief enough to be almost non-existent. 'Do you put on your shoes or shall I take you from here barefoot?'

Blindly she turned to obey, groping for them with her toes. 'I have some other things.'

'Leave them where they are.' He made no attempt to touch her, standing back to allow her passage from the room, then moving into place beside her along the white-walled corridor.

Grant's room was three down. Lian looked at the closed door and knew she couldn't leave it like this. In one swift movement her hand found the knob and pushed.

He was sitting on the bed facing the door, fully dressed in

jacket and trousers. Two of Ricardo's men from the *estancia* kept him company, one sitting, one leaning against the wall. The latter came swiftly upright on her entry, eyes going beyond her to his employer in the corridor.

'Lian, are you all right?' Grant demanded on a note of concern. He made an attempt to rise, only to sink back on to the mattress again with a wry shrug as his nearest companion gestured at him. 'These two apes have me outnumbered, I'm afraid.'

'These two "apes" have instructions to keep you here until your train is due in the morning,' came Ricardo's cold tones from the doorway. 'Think yourself fortunate to get away so lightly. There are less pleasant ways of dealing with men such as yourself.'

'Grant, listen to me,' Lian said urgently, aware that she wasn't going to have another chance. 'I want you to go away and forget about all this. I was going back anyway—I already told you that. I'm sorry for everything.'

He looked at her long and hard for a moment, then lifted his shoulders in resigned acceptance. 'So am I.'

Ricardo took her by the shoulder, his fingers scorching through the material of her suit. Without speaking, he propelled her from the room and closed the door, then along the corridor to the staircase at the end. The desk was deserted when they reached the lobby. They went straight through to the outer doors and into the street beyond where the car stood waiting.

They had left the town before Lian could bring herself to speak. 'I meant what I said back there,' she got out at last. 'I was coming back.'

'So it would appear.' His profile was hard and relentless against the night sky, his voice equally so. 'Via the coast, I assume?'

'No.' She spread her hands helplessly. 'I know you're not going to believe me——'

'Then there is little point in continuing the discussion,' he cut in. 'If you are wise you will stay quiet for the rest of our journey. I am in no mood for your British equality tonight.'

'We have to talk about it,' she came back on an edge of desperation. 'You can't just ignore what's happened.'

He said softly, 'I can do whatever I wish. That is something you still have to learn. When I returned from Tandil this afternoon, it was with the intention of telling you of a change in the terms of our agreement.'

'A—change?'

'I want a son.' The words were slow and measured. 'You will give me one.'

'No!' She had come upright in her seat, eyes blazing. 'I'd rather die first!'

'That is easy to say now,' on a hard mocking note, 'but life is very sweet. When I found you gone I wanted to kill you myself, only that would have defeated my purpose. You are fortunate.'

'The agreement was for six months,' Lian flung at him. 'You gave me your word!'

'You gave me *your* word too. It seems we are well suited.' For the first time since leaving the hotel he allowed the glittering anger to show in his glance. 'You said once that I was no different from my father, and perhaps you were right. He was a man who took what he wanted regardless of the feelings of others. Tonight I intend to do the same. From now onwards we live together as man and wife.' He paused as though expecting some word from her, lips tightening anew when she failed to say anything. 'On the day you present me with a son I will settle on you a sum sufficient to keep you in comfort for life. *Then* you can go to your Grant!'

She took in a quivering breath. 'You think I'd agree to that? You really believe I'd leave any child of mine with you?'

'The child,' he said, 'would be a Mendoza—an Argentinian.' His shrug was indifferent. 'However, as the mother you would have the right to stay with him should you wish it.'

Should she wish it! Lian stared at him with a sense of unreality, her mind refusing to accept the evidence of her ears. 'Why?' she asked at last in low, unsteady tones. 'Why are you doing this, Ricardo?'

He kept his eyes on the darkness ahead, the skin stretched taut over the bones of his face. 'Yesterday Carlos made the mistake of reminding me that without an heir Mendoza would one day revert to his side of the family. I am not going to let that happen.'

'How do you know I can even have children?'

'Why should I doubt it? You are young and healthy.'

'Fine breeding stock!' she retorted with bitter anger, and jerked forward in her seat as he brought the car to a sudden and violent halt. Hands reached for her, pulling her round and towards him, then his mouth was on hers in scorching, bruising passion, taking her senses and spinning them into response, blocking out thought of any kind at all.

The lift of his head left her defenceless. He was breathing fast and still blazing with fury, arms hurting her.

I am not an animal!' he said. 'There will be nothing cold and clinical about this union of ours. I shall make you hunger for my attentions! Like this! And this!' He was kissing her again, on her neck, on her throat, brushing aside the collar of her jacket to press his lips to the warmth below. 'Your heart leaps to me already,' he murmured against her skin. 'In a little while your whole body will crave for fulfilment— this I promise you. But first we return home. My son will not be conceived in such conditions as these!'

Lian sank into the corner of her seat as he let her go, her mind in a turmoil. Her skin tingled where his lips had touched her, a sensation both pleasurable and nerve-quivering at one and the same time. She was afraid of Ricardo, not just for what he could do to her physically, she realised, but for

what he could make her feel emotionally. She didn't want
to love him, she thought in desperation. How could she love
a man who would do what he was planning to do? No matter
what happened between them she must fight to stay aloof
from it all, to retain her identity. He could force her to surrender her body, but he could never claim possession of her
mind!

She was still huddled unmoving and silent in the corner of
her seat when they finally reached the *casa*. Ricardo helped
her from the car, his touch like fire on her forearm. There
was to be no reprieve, she gathered, on meeting the dark
smouldering gaze for a brief instant. He had meant every
word he had said. For him, as a man, love was the least
essential part of the affair. Why should she expect him to
recognise her needs?

Inez met them inside, her manner formal and unsmiling.
There was no triumph in the glance she rested momentarily
on Lian; there might even have been a fleeting compassion in
the dark eyes as they took in the pallor of her face. She
acknowledged her employer's request for a tray to be sent up
with a nod of her head, and disappeared in the direction of
the kitchens.

'Come,' Ricardo said without inflection, and started towards
the stairs, turning back when she failed to move with him
to take her under the elbow and urge her forward. 'Do not
force me to carry you to your room,' he said low-toned. 'That
would achieve you nothing but humiliation.'

'Don't you mean *further* humiliation?' she responded on
a high taut note, and felt the hand under her elbow harden
ruthlessly.

'You will not swerve me,' he stated, 'but you may very well
infuriate me beyond the point of caring whether you find
pleasure with me tonight or not. I am your husband and I
intend to share your bed, with or without your consent. The
choice is yours.'

Lian said no more. There seemed little use. She wasn't going to talk him out of this for certain.

Her room was no haven with him at her heels. He came no further than the door, however, allowing her to move away from him with a faint sardonic smile on his lips before going on towards his own room. Alone at last, Lian sat down heavily in the nearest chair and tried to come to terms with the situation. Ricardo had left her now, but he would be back—there was nothing surer than that. And when he came he would expect her to be prepared to comply with his demands—in fact, not merely to comply but to *respond*. He could make her respond too, she already knew that—if she let him. And there lay the crux of the matter. Did she bow her head to fate and accept what little compensation was offered her, or did she fight? Either way the end result would be the same.

Inez brought up the tray herself, setting it down on the low, inlaid table by the windows and straightening to her usual ramrod stiffness again to turn her head towards the slender figure of her mistress emerging from the bathroom.

'The soup is freshly made,' she proffered on a note distinctly softer than she had hitherto employed. 'You will find it tasteful, *señora*.'

Meeting the housekeeper's gaze, Lian registered the same gleam of womanly compassion she had seen downstairs, and at last recognised its basis. In the normal course of events a runaway wife could no doubt expect a beating from the husband who caught up with her, if nothing else. It was in all probability to this cause that Inez was attributing her present subduedness. She made an effort to smile as she thanked the woman. Sympathy, whatever its source, was balm to her spirit at this moment. She only wished that were all she did have to think about. Chastisement she could understand if not exactly appreciate. What Ricardo contemplated went beyond all.

She made no effort to touch the soup after Inez left, although she did try a few sips of coffee. The liquid tasted bitter and no amount of sugar seemed to help. She left it, and took a seat in one of the deep chairs, drawing her wrap closely about her with a quivering sensation as she waited for Ricardo to come. No use locking the door against him —in the mood he was in he would probably kick it down. This was his house, his home; and she was his wife. There was nowhere she could go to be safe from him.

When he did come it was quietly, letting himself into the room and closing the door gently behind him. He was wearing a black silk dressing gown over the lower half of a pair of matching pyjamas, his chest bare within the deep opened vee. A small medallion gleamed silver amidst dark hair.

'Is the soup not to your liking?' he asked, coming closer to where she sat.

Lian shook her head. 'I'm not hungry.' She looked up at him standing there in the subdued light and tried to read some element of tenderness into the hard, lean features. 'Ricardo——'

'No,' he said wearily. 'No more words. There have been more than enough between us.' He reached out and drew her to her feet, holding her lightly but firmly as he bent his head to find her mouth in a long, searching kiss.

She felt his hands at the fastenings of her wrap, then he was pushing it back and over her shoulders so that it slid from her to the floor. His arms came around her, lifting her as they had done that other night to carry her across to the bed, laying her down in the pillows without releasing her.

Deep down she felt the first faint stirrings of response, and knew that if she were going to fight at all it had to be now. Without allowing herself time to think about it she drew back her hand and hit him with all her strength in the face, taking advantage of his involuntary jerk backwards to roll away from him towards the edge of the bed. She didn't get very far. Even as she sat up, hands fastened on her shoulders

from behind, yanking her back and down again, pinning her
there helplessly as he loomed above her. Even in the semi-
darkness she could see the hand mark on the side of his
face where she had struck him, a trickle of red high on his
cheekbone where her ring must have caught.

'There is only one way with a woman such as you,' he
gritted through his teeth. 'You deserve no better!'

CHAPTER NINE

It was dawn when she awoke from the fitful sleep into which she had finally slipped. One arm was flung across her eyes as if to shut out the start of another day. Several moments passed before she could bring herself to remove it.

The pillow beside her own was wrinkled with usage but unoccupied. Ricardo had left her hours ago to return to his own room, sliding from the bed without a word either of comfort or remorse. Lian closed her eyes again tightly against the memories. He had shown no mercy in his possession of her, only the utter ruthlessness of a man bent on asserting his will. There had been no pleasure, only pain and degradation and the knowledge that it could all have been so very different had she chosen to submit. Well, she never would. Not now. She would fight him until he tired of having to take her by force!

She rose as soon as she heard movement in the courtyard below. Showered and dressed in the new jodhpurs Ricardo had brought back from Santina the night of Grant's arrival, she felt better equipped to cope with what the day must bring.

The quality of Pedro's greeting when she reached the stables gave her cause to wonder just how much the Mendoza staff knew of the previous day's happenings. News travelled fast in small communities; certainly they would all be aware of her departure, and the fact that Ricardo had been forced to fetch her back. She made every effort to appear her normal sef as Rojo was brought out to her, accepting the stable boy's offer of a leg up into the saddle with a lighthearted smile.

Diablo was in the corral, black coat gleaming in the sunlight. Fear that Ricardo might take it into his head to take an early morning ride himself got Lian moving quickly away from the house. She had to prepare herself to face him again in the cold light of day, to withstand the knowing contempt she was sure would be in his gaze. If she could cultivate a convincing enough air of indifference that would be one in the eye for him. Half his triumph must come from believing he had her thoroughly humbled by last night's experience, and reconciled to his demands. But she wasn't and wouldn't be, and the sooner he learned that the better.

The air was definitely cooler this morning, the mounting sun gentle on her skin. She reined Rojo in to sit gazing out to the far distant horizon, accustomed now to the vastness if not yet reconciled. If she gave Ricardo the son he wanted he would grow to love this land as his father did. It mustn't happen, she told herself fiercely. No matter what, she wouldn't have the child of a man who felt nothing for her!

He was already at breakfast in the courtyard when she returned to the house. She went down after tidying herself in her room, steeling her nerves to meet the dark appraisal when he lifted his head on her approach, knowing he was remembering as his glance moved over her, although his expression revealed little.

'You left no word with anyone as to your whereabouts,' he said.

'Pedro knew I'd taken Rojo,' she returned equably, sitting down at the table. She kept her features smooth and untroubled before his scrutiny, pouring fruit juice from the waiting pitcher and leaning back in the chair to sip from the glass with her eyes wandering over the sun-dappled stone of the central arch. 'It isn't as hot now as when I first came here,' she added on a conversational note. 'I'm going to need some heavier clothes if I'm to stay out the winter.'

'There is no "if" about it. You can obtain all you will need in Santina.'

She looked directly at him then. 'I'm actually to be allowed to visit the town again!'

Almost imperceptibly his jawline hardened. 'It is still not too late,' he said on a note of deliberation.

'You mean you might beat me if I don't show proper respect for my husband?'

His smile was faint and satirical. 'I mean I shall take you across my knee and spank you like the child you seem intent on staying.'

'Hardly a child,' she retorted. 'You made sure of that last night.'

It was a moment or two before he replied, his glance narrowed to her face with an expression hard to define. 'You expect me to apologise for that?'

'No.' She swallowed painfully. Where was her planned indifference now? 'No, I don't expect you to apologise. Why should you? I'm your property, after all. I suppose you're entitled to your full value!'

'And you believe that is what you supplied?'

This time she was unable to control the flush. 'It's the most you'll ever get from me!'

His shrug suggested all the indifference she could have hoped for herself. 'If you wish.'

It mattered little to him either way, she acknowledged heavily. But she had already known that, so why let it hurt afresh? Tonight, and on any other night he chose, he could come to her bed and exercise his so-called rights, and there was nothing she could do about it. Once he achieved his aim he might then leave her alone, only what a price to pay: a child conceived with such calculated lack of emotion. It didn't bear thinking about.

She forced herself to eat when Juanita brought food, although she felt no hunger. Her last meal before this had been breakfast yesterday, she realised in some small surprise. Odd how food became of such minor importance when the mind was under strain.

Ricardo left before she had finished toying with the meal. He didn't bother to say when he would be back. Alone again, she contemplated the day stretching ahead and knew she had to find something to occupy her mind or go mad. Grant would be on the train speeding coastwards by now. She could conjure no particular emotion over that either. Even if she had gone with him it would have been no use. She didn't love Grant; she didn't love anybody. Any capacity she had ever possessed for loving was drained from her for good.

The morning passed somehow. Lunchtime came and went and the afternoon stupor infiltrated the *casa* and its surrounds. Lian took a slow stroll down to the entrance archway of the estate, leaning under the shade of the stone to study the familiar landscape immediately adjoining with a mind kept carefully blank. She was still standing there when the cloud of dust coming up from the west resolved itself into the shape of a Land-Rover driven fast. Isabella was at the wheel, her lovely features set in lines of concern as she brought the vehicle to a stop close to where Lian waited.

'Is it true?' she asked without preamble. 'Do they lie when they say you try to run away with Señor Edwards?'

The grapevine certainly worked fast, Lian conceded. But then it would. News of any kind held import where there was so little.

'It's true,' she said. 'Ricardo caught up with us. Did you come to see him?'

'I come to see *you*.' Isabella slid from behind the wheel, smoothing down the skirt of her simple cotton dress. The long dark hair was tied back from her face with a scarf, emphasising her cheekbones under the smooth olive skin. 'Ricardo is not here?'

'No. Surprising, isn't it? You'd think he wouldn't trust me out of his sight so soon.' Lian's voice was deliberately bright. 'Of course, the fact that Grant is on his way to the coast might have something to do with it. I'm hardly going to cut out again on my own!'

'Lian, please do not be like this,' Isabella pleaded softly. 'If Ricardo has made you so unhappy that you feel you must leave him then he deserves little sympathy, but he is still your husband.'

'And as such merits lip service to loyalty,' Lian agreed on a rueful note. 'I'm sorry, Isabella, I shouldn't have said that just now. It will be all right, don't worry about it.'

'I cannot help but worry,' Isabella said. 'I love Ricardo and I hoped to be allowed one day to make a friend of his wife. What has happened between you only the two of you must know, but I had to come and see for myself the truth of the matter.' She paused, glancing towards the house in apparent indecision. 'There is something I must tell you, and yet I hardly know how to begin.'

'Shall we go indoors?' Lian suggested, but the other girl shook her head.

'No, that would not be right until I have Ricardo's blessing.'

'You mean until he reconciles himself to your marriage with Carlos?'

'That is a part of it.' She took a long slow breath, let it out again on a sigh. 'The enmity between my husband and yours has lasted too long. Nothing will ever be right between them until they each of them learn to stop hating the other for something which cannot be changed. Two days ago when you brought Señor Edwards to our home, Carlos——' she paused again, catching at her lower lip with her teeth and visibly forcing herself to continue—'Carlos told him the details of the story as he sees them, and suggested that your departure from Mendoza would solve many problems.' Her eyes appealed for understanding. 'Please do not judge him too harshly. He recognised Señor Edwards' attraction towards you, and thought you perhaps not entirely unreceptive.'

She deserved that, Lian acknowledge wryly. Carlos had a great deal more perception that she had given him credit for. She wondered how far the suggestion had influenced

Grant's actions. Not that it was of any real importance.

'I shan't judge him at all,' she said. 'I'm in no position to judge anybody.'

'Because you married Ricardo without giving yourself time to know him in any depth?' Her smile was that of a woman far beyond her years in understanding. 'It is said that no person can fully know another until they have lived together for a considerable length of time. Carlos is a stranger to me still in many ways, but we grow slowly closer because we both of us want to be close. There are things he does that I do not like and cannot condone, as I am sure he finds also in me. It is a part of marriage to learn tolerance of each other's faults, for we can rarely change them.' She went on slowly, 'I have known Ricardo for many years and he has always been a man difficult to reach. You will forgive me for thinking that perhaps you have not tried hard enough to reach him.'

Lian's head jerked. 'You know *why* he married me?'

'I know why he married you so quickly—that could not be hidden. But if fulfilment of the conditions was all he wanted why did he wait until it was almost too late? There are many who would have been only too glad to become the Señora Mendoza.'

But not with a limit on the engagement, Lian thought with irony. There was little point in going into that aspect of the affair now. Why disillusion Isabella any further?

'We'll work it out,' she said. 'My being English doesn't help.'

'You mean it makes it difficult for you to accept a man as your superior?' Isabella asked with unexpected humour. 'It is only an attitude one assumes for the sake of male pride—a small return, I think, for his love and protection. Does it hurt so much to say, Yes, Ricardo, when he lays down some minor rule of obedience? Even on your wedding night you had to challenge him. No man of pride will suffer the humiliation of failing to command respect from his womenfolk, and you should not expect it from him.' She seemed to catch herself up there, eyes and voice taking on a rueful expression. 'And I should not interfere in matters which are not my concern. Forgive me.'

Lian shook her head. 'There's nothing to forgive. We just have different viewpoints, that's all.' She hesitated before adding, 'How did Carlos take the loss of the sheep?'

The olive face clouded anew. 'Very badly.'

'And your father?'

'He blames Carlos for allowing them to wander on to Mendoza land.' Dark eyes lifted frankly. 'He has no part in any of this. His only wish is for Carlos to assume control of the Riga Estancia and stop the feud with his brother. In his eyes, Ricardo has the right to Mendoza.'

Lian said softly, 'Do you agree with him?'

Honesty fought with loyalty and effected a compromise. 'I think they should both of them agree to forget the past and be content with what they have. One day I may convince my husband, but only if you also try to reason with yours.' She stretched out and briefly touched her fingers to Lian's cheek. 'I must go now before I am missed. Carlos must not know I have been here. I hope there will come a time when we can be true friends.'

'So do I,' Lian answered with sincerity. 'And thank you for coming to see me, Isabella.'

'I felt it necessary, although I doubt if I have helped.'

Lian watched her get back into the car and start the engine, lifting a hand in farewell as she turned for home. There was a lot in what Isabella had said that made sense, but also a great deal which just didn't apply in this particular case. Ricardo couldn't care less whether she said yes *or* no, and that was indisputable fact.

Dinner that night was an ordeal. Lian ate what was put in front of her without tasting a thing, aware of the inexorable march of the clock and trying not to think ahead to the time when they would retire for the night. Would she have the courage, or even the fortitude, to put up a fight

against him again, she wondered—and even if she did was
it worth the effort when the outcome was already cut and
dried? What was it Victorian women used to do on such
occasions: close their eyes and think of England! It was at
least appropriate.

Stop it! she told herself fiercely at that point. It was no
joking matter. She took up the glass of wine with tense
fingers and lifted it to her lips, meeting Ricardo's gaze down
the length of the table as she tilted her head to take a drink.
He said nothing when she drained the glass, getting to his
feet to take the bottle and pour her more, then sitting down
again to resume his meal. She wondered what would happen
if she seized the refilled glass and hurled it across the room—
what was *left* to happen! There came a point, she realised,
when nothing mattered any more. He had already done his
worst; whatever came next would only be repetitive.

He put on a tape of classical music in the *salón*, coming
back to where she sat on the leather sofa to take the coffee
she had poured and seat himself close by. The haunting,
melancholy strains filling the room were vaguely familiar,
and particularly emotive right now.

'What is it?' she asked diffidently.

'Borodin,' he said. '*On the Steppes of Central Asia.*' He
glanced at her. 'You would prefer something a little lighter?'

She shook her head. 'No, I like it.' She saw his lip curl
faintly and made haste to amend the statement. 'That's hardly
the word. It stirs emotion.'

'It is meant to. One *feels* the bleakness and the poverty; the
endless toil of the peasant. It creates thankfulness for what
one has.'

For him, perhaps. At that moment Lian would almost
rather have been on the Russian Steppes herself.

They talked desultorily for another hour or so along
general, impersonal lines. It reminded Lian of those first
evenings here at Mendoza, except that the tension then had
not been nearly so prevalent. She would have given a lot to

know what was really going through Ricardo's mind as he sat there discussing the relative merits of the two most well-known Russian composers with such seeming attention. Was he amused by her efforts to dissimulate or appreciative of her need to do so? From where she sat she could see the tiny mark on his cheekbone where her ring had cut him. Tonight he would probably make sure that she took it off before he made love to her. Her thoughts paused there in quick cynicism. Love? What a meaningless word that had become when it could be used so unthinkingly as a euphemism for rape! And that was what it really was when a man forced his attentions on a woman, married to her or not. And it would happen again, because she wouldn't give in to him. She couldn't. Not now.

Eleven o'clock brought the realisation that one of them had to make the first move. Lian would not have put it past him to be purposely leaving it to her. Even that much initiative was something, she supposed. With an effort, she forbore from the pretence of a yawn to announce her intention. She wasn't in the least bit tired; she had never felt further from sleep.

'I'm going to bed,' she said on as level a note as she could manage, and got to her feet.

There was no visible reaction in his face as he leaned forward to life the brandy he had recently poured. '*Salud* !' he said.

It was temptation not to at least try locking her door when she reached her room, but what was the use? Ricardo was hardly a man to be deterred by hints. She prepared for bed quickly, heart thudding already like a trip-hammer in anticipation of his approach. Yet he was hardly likely to come straight to her. There were rituals to be observed in this Latin household, tradition to be upheld in the aim of keeping desire alive. He would go first to his own room as he had last night, savouring the knowledge of her helplessness against him, drawing out the minutes until he thought he had her suitably strung up. Then and then only would he come to make his demands.

She was lying staring at the ceiling of the darkened room when she finally heard his footsteps in the corridor. They passed her door without pausing, and she heard his own door close quietly. Minutes ticked by in slowly increasing procession, each one adding to the turmoil inside her. Stop taunting me, she begged silently. Get it over!

It was almost an hour before she could be sure he wasn't going to come to her, and a further two before she slept.

In the days which followed there were to be many times when the memory of those sleepless hours would return to haunt her. Gradually she developed a mental block against emotion of any kind. Whatever happened from here on in would do so regardless of how much she agonised over it, so let it be. Ricardo would decide.

He seemed in no hurry, she had to admit. His manner towards her retained the same basis of cool appraisal. It was as if he waited for her to make some move or other first. Well, he would wait a long time because she was through with sticking her neck out. Apathy was her best weapon.

The slight softening in attitude displayed by Inez remained unexpectedly in evidence. Knowing the woman's regard for her employer and long-standing loyalty to the Mendoza family, Lian was surprised yet somehow comforted to find the stiffness relaxed to even this small extent. The first time Inez asked her what she would like ordered for dinner that same evening, it was on the tip of her tongue to tell her to order what she herself thought suitable, until she realised the concession was a subtle way of underlining her position as mistress of the household. She wasn't, and never would be, but there was no way of putting that across to Inez. She smiled instead and itemised the first dishes which occurred to her off-hand, realising that from now on she had better get down to thinking seriously about her duties, no matter how temporary.

It was after the meal that evening that Ricardo finally made a move towards disturbing the pattern of the last week.

'The days grow cooler,' he announced casually. 'If we are to make that trip to the Sierras it should be now.'

Lian did not turn from her contemplation of the court-yard through the open doors of the *salón*. 'I've changed my mind,' she said without expression.

'But I have not.' His tone was soft, though with an edge to it. 'We will leave in the morning and camp for two nights. You are well enough accustomed to the saddle to spend whole days in it without too much discomfort.'

She turned then, meeting the implacable dark eyes. 'You intend to ride all the way up there?'

'Naturally. I told you before there were many places where a car cannot go.' He studied her a moment, and very subtly his tone changed. 'It will be good for both of us to be away from Mendoza for a time.'

She said with emphasis, 'It won't make any difference to the way I feel.'

The inclination of his head was unexpected. 'No,' he agreed, 'it is up to me to make a difference in the way you feel. When you come down from the Sierras it will be as a woman versed to some small extent in the art of pleasing a man.' His regard grew satirical again. 'This time you will not goad me to anger so that you may wallow in your martyr-dom!'

'You can lead a horse to water——' she quoted, conscious of her quickening pulses.

'It depends upon the thirst,' he said. 'Your English pro-verbs have no bearing here. My son will not be born to the kind of atmosphere which exists between us now.'

Lian made herself hold the mocking gaze. 'Supposing I gave you a daughter?' she said. 'What then?'

His shrug was unconcerned. 'The chances are small. From far back the Mendozas have always fathered more sons than daughters.'

'I'll remind you of that if it happens.'

'You will not need to remind me of anything. The male is directly responsible.' He paused, expression unchanging. 'Should it happen, then we would have to try again, would we not?'

'It's all so—so cold-blooded!' she burst out passionately, and drew a lift of his eyebrow.

'You are not listening. It is because my blood is *not* cold that I insist on your own not being so either.' He held out a hand to her from where he sat on one of the sofas. 'Come here to me now.'

She stiffened. 'No!'

'You would prefer that I fetch you?' His voice hadn't risen, but the inflection was sharper. 'Come *here*!'

There was little use in defying him. He would probably take delight in making her do as he bade her. She went over, dropping with deliberation to her knees in front of him, eyes flashing a challenge. 'Is this subservient enough for you, or shall I put my head under your foot?'

His own eyes sparked in answer, his hands coming out to clasp either side of her face and draw her towards him, his knees pinioning her.

'It is not your subservience I look for,' he gritted. 'But if it is your need to be forcibly subdued——'

'No.' The word was jerked from her, the reckless impulse already regretted. 'Don't!'

His grasp on her tightened cruelly. 'Say please. That is a word you use all too rarely, *chica*! Say please, Ricardo, to let you go, and then I will think about it.'

With his mouth bare inches from hers she could not find the will to refuse. 'Please,' she got out, and heard him laugh.

'It chokes you, does it not, to ask my indulgence? Do my kisses stir you to such fear, or is it your own reaction to

them you dare not test again right now?' One thumb traced
a line down from her cheekbone to her lips, following the
curve with nerve-quivering sensitivity. 'Before too long,' he
said very softly, 'you will be saying please to me for quite
another reason. Tomorrow night we will lie together under
the stars and make love the way it should be between a man
and a woman. You will not lash out at me because you will
have no desire to do so. That is a promise to take to your
bed with you tonight.'

He stood up then, drawing her with him, holding her in
front of him for a long moment more, looking into her
darkened green eyes with an expression hard to define before
letting go of her. 'Go now and get your rest. You are going
to need it for the journey tomorrow.'

She was going to need more than that, Lian acknowledged numbly as she left him. She was going to need every
ounce of will-power she possessed to resist the claims he could
make on her emotions.

CHAPTER TEN

The morning was already well advanced by the time they eventually left, due to the interminable last-minute problems the Estancia managers kept bringing up. Rojo was skittish, sidling up to Diablo like some mischievous child whenever he found an opportunity, until Ricardo curtly commanded Lian to keep him under control.

'I can't,' she said woodenly. 'He doesn't respond to the reins.'

'Only because you are not firm enough. An animal is always quick to take advantage.'

And a woman; he didn't have to say it, she knew what that curl of his lip implied. She watched his hands on Diablo's reins, never cruel but allowing no quarter either. He treated the horse better than he had treated her at times, she thought, and knew that was unfair. What she had suffered at his hands she had asked for to a great extent.

They were travelling light, each horse carrying only a minimum load in addition to its rider. There was a tent in Diablo's pack, because she had seen it, but it would probably only be used in case of rain. They would lie under the stars, Ricardo had said last night, and he had meant exactly that. Blankets were his only concession to creature comforts. What extra warmth was needed they would gain from each other.

'How long will it take us to reach the hills?' she asked now, with her eyes on the distant line.

'Five, perhaps six hours, if we go steadily. There is no hurry.'

'None at all,' she agreed dryly, and felt his glance flick over her, in mockery.

'You are not looking forward to being alone with me tonight?'

'I've been alone with you before.'

He refused to rise to the jibe. 'That is in the past. You will soon forget what it was like before.'

The tautening of her fingers caused Rojo to jerk his head in protest. 'I'll *never* forget,' she said with passion, 'because it won't be any different, tonight or any other night! I won't come to you willingly, Ricardo!'

His smile was slow. 'The day will be long. You will have little strength left to fight me, *chica*.'

'Is *that* why you're dragging me all this way on horseback?'

'We go to the Sierra because you once expressed a wish to see it.'

'Oh, I see. You're just trying to please me.'

For a fleeting moment the familiar fire blazed in his eyes, then was swiftly controlled.

'You are not going to rouse my anger with words,' he said. 'You have done that too often in the past. This time you will face your true emotions without that defence.'

Her true emotions—Lian only wished she knew what they were. She could tell herself she hated him, but that was only a part of it. He was right about it being a defence, of course, only how deep did the feelings it covered up really go? Not that it made any difference. If she once had Ricardo's child she was committed to staying with him anyway. Even now she might be carrying that child, although she prayed she was not. Conception without love would be bad enough, but infinitely better than that.

She knew then that the fight was over, and the knowledge brought an odd sort of peace. If she were bound already to this marriage then she was also bound to try making it as good as it could be. Ricardo might not love her, but he needed her, if only as the mother of his son. Perhaps from those beginnings they could build something worthwhile.

If he sensed any change in her attitude he gave no sign of it. They stopped to eat at one o'clock when the sun had already begun its incline westwards, lighting the tiny portable gas stove to boil water for coffee because of the lack of wood with which to make an open fire. The hills looked appreciably closer now, ridged and rocky, with cloud peppering the sky above them. In front and to either hand spread the broad vista of the plain, dotted here and there with groups of cattle and sheltering clumps of trees, endless in its expanse.

'Do you still feel you hate this place?' Ricardo asked quietly, watching Lian's face as she viewed the scene.

She glanced his way, remembering that first night he had brought her here to the *pampas* and the proclamation she had made. 'I'm getting used to it,' she said. 'It takes time.'

'Doesn't everything? Perhaps the realisation is half the battle.'

Lian said on impulse, 'You know, that's the first time I've ever heard you use a contraction in English speech.'

He shrugged and laughed. 'It was quite unstudied. I learned to speak your language from books and in school. It is only on living with it daily that one begins to lose the stilted perfection. You yourself speak Spanish with a far more natural style than when you first came. You have even, I noticed, picked up some of the local dialect—from your talks with Juanita, perhaps.'

She caught his eye uncertainly. 'Do you object to my chatting with her? She was terribly shy about it herself at first.'

'Until you drew her out.' He paused. 'Why should I object?'

'Custom. I thought it might not be the done thing to have any personal contact with the servants.'

'But you didn't let it stop you.' He had used the contraction deliberately this time; she could tell that from the way he had said it with a faint smile on his lips. 'Any ruling along those lines can only be in your own mind. I see no reason why you and Juanita should not be friendly, providing you don't encourage her to become dissatisfied with her place in life. Strange as it may appear to you, the Mendoza household staff consider themselves already among the élite of their kind.'

'So I've gathered.' Lian hesitated before going on, aware of the tenuous balance of this present sociability. 'The Mendozas go back a long way, don't they?'

'A very long way,' he agreed. 'I can trace my Argentinian ancestry back to the Pedro de Mendoza who first established the settlement which became Buenos Aires.'

'The Spanish invaders!' She couldn't resist the dig, though she made it a suitably light one.

'True.' He poured more coffee, sitting back on one bent leg with the other raised to support his elbow as he regarded her. 'Just as the English colonised so many other lands. The white man has always been acquisitive. Land; power; wealth,' —the pause stretched, his eyes taunting—'women.'

'In that order?' she queried blandly, and he laughed.

'It would depend on one's priorities.' The smile disappeared again, a faint line appearing instead between his brows. 'Without a woman I would have lost two of the other three.'

It was impossible to keep the edge of bitterness from her voice. 'I only hope it's worth it.'

There was no readable expression in the look he gave her. 'I hope so too. Are you ready to go on?'

The afternoon was drawing towards its close when they finally reached the hills. Ricardo took the lead as they began to climb along the line of a narrow defile, the horses picking their way surefooted among the rocks. Grass still cloaked these lower slopes. Only as they got higher did it gradually give way to larger and larger patches of bare rock, the ground opening into ravines or towering in craggy bluffs, the whole landscape so vastly different from that to which Lian had become almost inured she lost count of time or distance in her study of it.

The plateau when they reached it reminded her of parts of the Yorkshire Dales, a region of rough moorland interspaced with jutting rock, lonely and desolate. With the sun sinking fast, Ricardo found a place to camp within the shelter of a small depression formed by several rocks. It was noticeably cooler up here, yet not uncomfortably so. There were some twiggy bushes in the vicinity, and even a few stunted trees. With a fire going the closing night lost its unfriendliness.

There was no actual need of the tent as there had been no sign of rain, yet Lian was thankful when Ricardo erected it without bothering to ask her opinion. It was somewhat larger than she had anticipated, adequate for two people without difficulty. She left him to arrange the blankets and other bedding inside while she fried steaks for supper, avoiding his eyes when he came back to the fire because she didn't want to think about later. She would take each moment as it came, that was the best way.

Ricardo made up the fire again after they had eaten, leaning back against a convenient boulder with every sign of staying put for some time. Hands clasped comfortably behind his head and eyes closed, his face highlighted by the flickering glow, he said very softly, 'This is good, you agree?'

'Yes,' she answered from the other side of the fire, and saw his eyes come open to look at her.

'You have reservations,' he said. 'Do you dread the touch of my hands?'

She shook her head, drawing a satirical smile.

'Then you should, if you meant what you told me earlier on today. If I am forced to subdue you I shall do so, believe me.'

'You won't have to.' The words were torn from her. 'I'll do my duty.'

'Your—duty?'

'Isn't that what you're after? A docile, biddable wife who fulfils her marriage contract in every way!'

'I think,' he said after a moment, 'that I would rather have you fight me again!'

'Well, I shan't.'

'I see.' Suddenly he was amused. 'You hope by appearing quiescent to dull my interest, perhaps? It won't work, *niña*. Neither, I assure you, will it last.'

'Don't be too sure!'

'But I am sure,' he said. 'A man cannot afford uncertainty —in life or in love. You will give yourself to me not out of any sense of duty but because this is what you want. And tonight I shall satisfy both our needs, I promise you that.'

'For the sake of an heir to Mendoza.' Her voice was low.

'Not altogether.' He was lying propped up on one elbow now, his eyes glinting with tawny lights as he looked at her through the flames. 'I want you, Lian. I wanted you the first night we met, but one cannot have everything. I had other priorities then—more important ones, as I thought. I looked no further than fulfilling the immediate terms of my father's will.'

'And promised me my freedom when you had,' she reminded him.

'As you promised me loyalty.' He gave a small sigh. 'We have been through all this before.'

'I know.' She clasped her knees with both arms, staring into the flames with concentration. 'You never asked me how I really felt about Grant.'

'I had no need.' There was an edge to his voice. 'You used him as a means of escape from a situation you could no longer cope with. He meant no more to you than that.'

'Oh, I see, *he* was the innocent party!'

'That was not what I meant, and well you know it. But had I believed him totally to blame he would not have escaped as lightly either. You both of you betrayed my trust.'

'You're a fine one to talk!' Her head was up, her jaw set against any betraying quiver. 'You'd already decided to change the terms of our agreement before you even knew about my going away with Grant. You admitted that yourself.'

'So we make a pair.' The tone was unmoved. 'It is somewhere to start.'

One of the horses tethered out beyond the circle of light snickered softly and was answered by the other, the sound changing to a sudden snort as some animal gave a short barking cry from not too far away.

'Jackal,' Ricardo supplied, watching her face. 'They will not come near the fire.' He stirred himself to reach for more fuel and pile it on, dusting off his hands on the seat of his pants as he came easily to his feet. 'That should last for some time.'

Lian didn't stir, conscious of his lean height and hard strength; of the dark curl of hair along muscular forearms bared by the rolled sleeves of his shirt. She remembered the feel of those arms, unyielding as iron bands, and knew a swift rush of thankfulness that tonight was going to be different.

When he came round the fire and drew her to her feet, she went unresistingly, meeting his lips halfway, feeling those same arms lift and hold her in an embrace from which she had no desire to escape.

It was cool beneath the canvas, the light from the fire outside dancing and flickering across roof and walls. His lovemaking was everything she had hoped for, his hands gentle yet so exquisitely sure, his voice caressing, murmuring endearments in his own language in between kisses, drawing her on to abandon all reticence and return passion for passion until nothing else mattered in the whole world but being one with Ricardo.

Afterwards, holding her with her head resting on his chest, he said softly, 'Now you are fully a woman, little one, how do you feel?'

'Grateful,' she said, and hoped he wouldn't hear the catch in her voice. 'You're a wonderful lover, Ricardo.'

'Thank you.' There was irony in the reply. 'It is good to know one's efforts are appreciated.'

She lifted her head a little to look at him in the shadow-filled light, trying, without success, to read what lay behind the dark eyes. 'Would you rather I told you I loved you instead?'

He looked back at her without altering expression. 'Would it be true?'

She allowed a moment to pass before slowly shaking her head. 'No.'

'Then there is little point in saying it,' he returned. 'No more than there would be in my saying it to you.' He drew her back to him with cool deliberation to put his lips to the hollow of her throat. 'We will simply make the most of what we have—like this. The night is still young, *querida*.'

She awoke when the weight of his arm left her waist, turning her head on the folded blanket which had acted as a pillow to see him sit up and reach for his clothing. Daylight filtered through the canvas; she could hear the horses moving restlessly.

She lay quietly while he dressed, seeing the muscle ripple smoothly beneath bronzed skin, remembering everything that had passed between them with an emotion that mingled guilt and contentment in almost equal amounts. When he looked round and saw her watching him she felt the blush starting deep. It was no surprise to see his brows lift in mocking acknowledgement.

'I am going to relay the fire for breakfast,' he said. 'There is no need for you to get up yet. I will call you when all is ready.'

'All right.' Lian badly wanted him to reach back and kiss her—just a light greeting such as any morning-bearded husband might give to his wife—but he made no attempt. She sat up as the tent flap dropped back into place, running a hand over her tousled hair and wondering suddenly what on earth she must look like. The sight of her scattered clothing brought more recollections. She made haste to dress, hoping there was going to be some way she could freshen up.

The fire was lit, the coffee pot already standing on its iron support at the outer edge of the flames when she got outside. She wasn't wearing a watch, but from the look of the sun it had to be going along for eight o'clock.

'Is there any spare water?' she asked awkwardly. 'I'd like to wash.'

Ricardo nodded his head towards a cleft between the two biggest rocks. 'If you go through there you'll find a whole pool of it. It stands much longer on the surface up here. You would like eggs for breakfast?'

'Well, yes.' She hesitated. 'But can't I do them when I get back?'

His shrug was easy. 'If you wish. I will come with you to the pool. You have a towel?'

'I don't know where they are.'

He went back to the tent, emerging a moment later holding two, one of which he handed over.

'The soap we must share,' he said, slinging his own towel over one shoulder. 'If you want to keep your hair dry you should take something with you to fasten it up out of the way.'

Lian glanced at him sharply. 'My hair dry?'

'Of course. The pool is usually deep enough to swim in. That is one of the reasons why I chose this place to camp last night. You do swim, of course?'

'Yes.' She stood there irresolutely, knowing he was laughing at her but unable to put a cool face on it. 'I—I didn't bring a suit.'

This time the laughter was open. 'Is that important? My eyes were not closed last night.'

Her face warmed. 'That was different.'

'I'm glad you think so.' He started to move in the direction he had indicated. 'Come.'

'Ricardo.' She stood her ground, waiting for him to turn back to look at her, ignoring the twist of his lips. 'Are you trying to humiliate me?' she demanded.

'Humiliate you?' He looked first astonished, and then suddenly and disconcertingly angry. Mouth tight, he drew the towel from over his shoulder and tossed it across a guy-rope. 'I should like to humiliate you!' he said. 'Are you still so immature that you need the cover of darkness before you dare to show yourself to me?'

'It has nothing to do with maturity,' she came back, angry herself now. 'I'm entitled to privacy when I want it!'

'You are entitled to nothing unless I care to grant it to you.' His tone was soft but his eyes were hard. 'What does it take to bring that fact home to you? You are my wife; my possession. What I tell you to do you will do!' He studied her a moment longer and made an impatient gesture. 'Go and take your bathe alone, if you must, my little prude. There is still a great deal you have to learn about the relationship between a husband and wife.'

The pool lay in a depression much like the one she had left, securely held by the rock base which formed these high Sierras. The water was cold enough to take her breath, and deep enough towards the centre for the bottom to be out of reach of a probing foot. She came out glowing, to rub herself quickly dry on the towel, dreading a return to Ricardo's sardonic gaze. He didn't understand, of course. He couldn't be expected to understand. Last night he had held her like this in his arms, warm and unprotesting, delighting even, in her power to stir him. To him daylight simply brought a new dimension to their knowledge of one another. Had real love existed between them she could imagine herself capable of the same attitude, but it didn't. Professor Higgins had had the right idea, she thought with an attempt to humour; why *couldn't* a woman be more like a man? Their needs were so much simpler.

He had shaved when she returned to the camp. He said nothing to her, reaching for his own towel and vanishing between the rocks. She made omelettes with the eggs when she judged him about ready to come back, sliding one on to a heated tin plate as he did so and handing it to him along with a fork.

'What are we going to do today?' she asked for want of anything better to say as he squatted to eat.

He shrugged. 'Return to Mendoza, perhaps.'

She looked at him in confusion. 'But I thought—you said two days, at least.'

His eyes met hers unsmilingly. 'It makes little difference. Whether here or back at Mendoza, I will stand no more of this childish censure.'

'Censure?' Lian tried to sound calm about it. 'Because I refused to join you in a nude swim?'

'You think that is all there is to it?' he demanded. 'You really believe my only interest lies in placing you in humiliating circumstances so that I may enjoy your discomfiture?' He put down the plate with a resounding clatter, the omelette only half eaten, anger in the set of his lips. 'Has it occurred to you that I might very easily have achieved such an aim by using your refusal as an excuse to make you do as I asked? Would the humiliation have been greater or less for your lack of choice in the matter?'

She shook her head miserably. 'You misunderstood. I wasn't censuring you, I was—embarrassed.'

The smile was mirthless. 'You were not embarrassed when I held you in my arms and caressed you. When I——'

'Ricardo!' Her cheeks were hot. 'That's not fair!'

'You mean it isn't right,' he said inexorably. 'You have this feeling of guilt because you enjoyed the lovemaking of a man with whom you are not in love, but you tell yourself you were given no choice and that salves your conscience. To make our marriage even begin to work, therefore, I must give you no choice in anything, then the blame is all mine. So that is how it will be from now on.'

She flared then. 'It was never any different!'

'You think not? I will have to prove it to you.' He straightened abruptly. 'Get your things together. We return to Mendoza.'

They neither of them spoke again while the tent was taken down and packed and the horses saddled. In the same silence, he gave her a leg up on to Rojo's back, muttering some brief expletive under his breath as the saddle moved beneath her weight.

'You did not tighten the girths,' he said. 'Move your leg to the side.'

Lian did so, looking down on the dark head with a hard misery in her chest. This marriage of theirs would never work. Not under these conditions. She wondered how he would react if she gave way to impulse now and allowed her hand to touch that darkness. She didn't have the courage to find out. With the strap adjusted satisfactorily, he moved away to mount Diablo, swinging the stallion's head at once in the direction from which they had come the previous day.

They were barely halfway down to the plain when the accident happened. It was Rojo who caused it by jerking forward on a particularly steep section of the trail in an effort to catch up with Diablo ahead, and losing his footing. Lian saw Ricardo stop and turn in the saddle, saw Diablo's ears go back as he felt Rojo's chest come up against his quarters and a sudden blur of movement as he reared and spun before crashing sideways to the ground.

He was up again almost immediately, blowing and snorting with fear, hooves narrowly missing the still, prone figure of his master lying where he had fallen with the side of his head on bare rock. Lian was down from the gelding before she had time to think about it, leaving the reins loose along his neck as she darted forward to seize the stallion's up close by the bit and throw all her weight into wheeling him away from Ricardo, heedless of her own danger from the sharp, dancing hooves. Then he was cantering off along the trail with Rojo in his wake and she could drop to her knees beside the horribly still body of the man she had married and try to assess the damage.

He was alive but unconscious, his breathing ragged and shallow, his face drained of colour except where the great darkening abrasion scarred his temple. His hair was already matted with blood and dust, the former running freely down the side of his face and neck to soak into the collar of his shirt. Somehow, Lian dragged her mind back from within the blank curtain of fear. Panic helped no one. First of all she must stem the bleeding!

The horses had stopped some hundred yards or so down the trail, standing in that lost attitude animals adopt when uncertain of their next move. Both were carrying water bottles. She took the one from Rojo's saddle, not caring to approach the stallion, whose black flanks still quivered with shock.

Ricardo hadn't moved when she got back. Tearing the spare shirt she had brought in the pack, she soaked strips of it in the clean water and gently cleansed the area immediately surrounding the wound. The bleeding was slowing of its own accord by now, starting to congeal in a sticky mass. She let well alone, and used another couple of pieces of shirt as a pad and bandages.

Her own limbs were trembling by the time she had finished, but there was more to do. Lying here right in the full glare of the sun couldn't be good for a head injury. She had to get him into the shade of the rocks.

How she accomplished it she never quite knew. He was a sheer dead weight, legs trailing in the dust as she dragged him bodily across the blessedly few yards, arms limp and hanging. She made him as comfortable as she could once she reached a level spot, with a sweater rolled up under his head as a pillow. After that there was little she could do but wait, crouching at his side with a prayer on her lips and a creeping dread in her heart. He couldn't die. He *mustn't* die! Oh, God, if only there were someone near to help her! She knew so little about these things.

Almost an hour had passed before he stirred with a faint groan. He came to slowly, eyes flickering open in blank appraisal of her face bent anxiously over him until they focussed on a spark of recognition.

'What—happened?' he got out, and she was dismayed by the slurred quality of the words.

'Diablo fell and threw you,' she said. 'You hit your head on the rocks. Don't try to talk, Ricardo. Please! There may —there may be a serious injury.'

He put up an unsteady hand and touched his fingers to the dressing, wincing as he did so. 'How—long?'

'About forty minutes. There has to be at least concussion. You mustn't move.'

'I have to move,' he said, sounding a little less shaky. 'I cannot just stay here.' He put out the same hand to a nearby spur of rock and levered himself to a sitting position, his face draining anew with the strain. His eyes closed again and for a horrible moment Lian thought he had slipped back into unconsciousness. When he did open them it was with an obvious effort, a faint rueful smile touching his lips. 'It appears I was wrong. Movement is going to be difficult. Are the horses close?'

She nodded, biting back tears of concern. 'Not far away.'

'Then bring them,' he said in a ghost of his normal commanding tones. 'Once in the saddle I shall manage.'

'You can't,' she said pleadingly. 'Ricardo, you can't possibly ride in this condition! Please don't try. Please!'

He looked at her for a long hard moment, eyes narrowed against the pain. 'There is no alternative.'

'There is. I can ride for help.' Her voice was eager. 'I can leave you water and food, and you're shaded from the sun. We could be back for you long before nightfall.'

'Only if you rode like the wind to reach the Estancia.' He caught her hand, holding it flat against his chest, his mouth firming. 'No, Lian, I won't allow it! You do not have the experience to make such a ride.'

'There's no alternative,' she said with deliberation. 'And you can't stop me. You're in no fit state to stop me.'

'You would take advantage of that?'

'Yes, if I have to.' She met his eyes and tried to smile. 'It's for your own good.'

'It is your good I am thinking of,' he returned with forced intensity. 'In a little time I will be ready to ride. I forbid you to go.'

It was some measure of his weakness that he couldn't hold on to the hand he was clasping when she exerted the pull. 'I'm sorry, Ricardo,' she said softly. 'I don't want to leave you, but I have to. I'll fetch the things.'

Rojo's movement towards her as she approached brought an exclamation of dismay to her lips. He was limping badly, favouring his left foreleg. She caught at his rein to halt him, then bent and ran her hand over the leg. There was no doubting the swelling just above the pastern. Diablo must have caught him when he backstepped to rear. One thing was certain, there would be no gallop across the *pampa* for the gelding. Which left only the stallion.

The latter laid back his ears as she went towards him, but made no move to back away. There was dust and some blood on the side where he had fallen, though the visible injuries appeared only superficial. Lian made no immediate attempt to touch him, standing where he could see her and smell her and willing herself to exude confidence.

'It's going to have to be the two of us, boy,' she said quickly. 'You're going to have to help me. Stay there and think about it. I'll be back.'

Ricardo was still in the same position against the rock

when she got back to him, eyes closed, face like death. He opened them as she came up, looking at the things she dumped on the ground beside him without expression.

'I thought you'd be more comfortable with the blankets,' she said. 'If I spread them here under the lee of the rock will you lie down?'

'I seem to have little choice,' he said. 'When I attempt to stand the world goes black.' The sigh held resignation. 'At least Rojo is a steady ride. Let him choose his pace. I have no fear of the dark.'

She was thankful the horses were out of sight from here. What he didn't know wouldn't hurt him. 'I will,' she promised. 'Is there anything else you need?'

His lips twisted briefly. 'Patience, perhaps. But that is something I must supply. Take care, little one. You are not to return with the car—just tell José where I am to be found.'

She didn't answer that one. She didn't want to go and leave him here alone either, but it was needs must. On impulse she bent and pressed her lips to the dirt-streaked cheek, jumping up before he could speak and hurrying away from him.

Diablo was standing where she had left him. She took a deep breath before reaching for his reins. He allowed her to lead him across to the nearest convenient rock for mounting, showing signs of restlessness only when she put her foot tentatively into the stirrup.

'Steady, boy!' she breathed. 'Oh, please, Diablo, don't let me down!'

The huge head swung towards her, eyes rolling. Heart in mouth, she swung her leg swiftly across the saddle and found the far stirrup, keeping the reins tight against the animal's sudden side-skittering reaction, and using her knees to urge him forward. 'Get on!' she cried in Spanish. 'Go, Diablo!'

There was a moment when she thought he was going to refuse to obey her commands, then suddenly his head went forward and he was springing into a canter, taking the bit between his teeth with a strength she knew she could never control. She pushed herself far down into the saddle, searching desperately for balance, feeling the surge of powerful muscles doing their utmost to unseat her.

Somehow she was still there when they reached the flat, too busy fighting for retention of what small directional command she possessed to feel any fear as he stretched into a gallop. She wasn't going to Mendoza; she had known that from the start. Riga was closer by several miles. There was just a chance she might make it before falling off.

CHAPTER ELEVEN

SHE didn't fall off, although it was touch and go on many occasions. As the miles fell behind them even Diablo's strength began to tire, his pace slowing to a point where Lian was able to get a real hold on his mouth again.

After that it was relatively easy, providing she disregarded the aching muscles of her legs and back. There would be time enough to think about discomfort when her journey was finished. For now the important thing was simply *to* finish it.

The stallion was walking when they finally came in sight of the Riga *casa*, head drooping, body steaming with sweat. Somebody saw them coming and gave the alarm, bringing people running from all directions as Lian slid wearily to the ground. Isabella and Carlos came together, the former wide-eyed with concern.

'What has happened?' she demanded, her gaze taking in the exhausted animal with sudden fear. 'Why are you riding Diablo?'

'It's Ricardo,' Lian got out. 'He's hurt, back in the hills.' Instinctively she turned to Carlos, seeing the bleakness of his features with sinking heart. 'I need help. You were closest. He hit his head—there may be a fracture. I——' She broke off with a muffled sob, pushing the back of her hand across her mouth to stop it. 'Please,' she begged, 'you have to help him, Carlos. He could die!'

The hardness of his features did not relax. 'If he dies,' he said, 'Mendoza will belong to you.'

'I don't want it. Not without your brother.' She used the word with purpose, searching for some lever to get below the

160

shell of indifference. 'He's my husband, Carlos, and I love him. As Isabella loves you.' It was true, she thought in aching acknowledgement, she did love him. Against her will, against her judgment; against every known reason, she loved him. And she wasn't about to let him die because this man in front of her now hated him as much as she had once believed she did. 'Your father is the one you should blame for all this!' she cried with passion. 'Not each other! You can't leave him out there. I won't *let* you leave him!'

'Carlos!' Isabella was at his side, clutching his arm, her face pleading. *'Favor!'*

Something seemed to deflate behind the brooding dark eyes as they turned from one white face to the other, and his shoulders sagged. 'I will have a car prepared,' he said. 'We will need a mattress laid into the back of the station wagon, and pillows.'

His wife put her hands against his chest and kissed him on the lips, her eyes filled with tears. *'Gracias, mi morido!* Lian, you must rest. Diablo will be taken care of.'

Lian handed over the stallion's reins to the waiting boy without hesitation, but shook her head to the other injunction. 'No, I'm going back with the car.'

'But you cannot! Not after riding so long and so far. Carlos, tell her she is not to go!'

His smile held irony. 'She is Ricardo's woman, not mine. There is time for some refreshment before we leave.'

Lian said softly, 'Thank you, Carlos.'

'I only do this because you and my wife ask it,' he returned with harsh inflection. 'It alters nothing. Ricardo himself will not thank you for coming to me.'

'It is probably true,' Isabella agreed as her husband left them to see to the car. 'They are both of them stubborn enough to prefer even death to any form of obligation where the other is concerned. But that is something they must sort out between them. Come, I must see to the fetching of a mattress and pillows for Ricardo's comfort on the journey home. It will be a long and slow one, for you will have to go slowly in case you are right about the fracture.' Her face was drawn. 'I hope you are not.'

'So do I,' Lian agreed from the heart. 'I've never wanted to be more wrong about anything!'

'You are limping,' the other observed as they moved through to the courtyard. 'Your legs are sore?'

'A little.' Not for all the tea in China would Lian have admitted to the real extent of the pain searing the inside of her thighs whenever she moved. The jodhpurs had saved a great deal of her skin, but her riding hours had not been sufficient to harden it against the friction of that initial mad gallop. She could only thank heaven she did not have to mount a horse again. Rojo would follow the car. 'It's only stiffness,' she hastened to add, afraid that Isabella would guess the truth and find some way of keeping her here. 'I'm not used to riding quite so far in one go.'

She waited restlessly with a barely touched drink when Isabella had gone to arrange for the things to be taken out to the car, not really trusting Carlos to keep his word. How long did it take to fill a tank with petrol? she wondered in rising suspicion as time passed. And why didn't Isabella come back?

It took the sound of an engine to bring the truth home. They were going without her! She was on her feet and running for the archway as Isabella came out from the house, ignoring the startled cry. The car was heading from the big main entrance arch; she changed direction to intercept it, anger lending her speed and the strength to disregard the pain in her legs. Carlos saw her coming, and said something to his driver, who brought the car to a halt.

'I'm coming with you!' Lian tore open the near rear door and flung herself in on top of the mattress occupying the whole of the back area, rolling over with a glare that defied Carlos to get her out again. 'I *won't* be left behind!'

Her brother-in-law shrugged broad shoulders and gave in.

'Ricardo must deal with you himself,' he growled. He ordered the car into motion again, turning his back on her.

It had taken Lian something like four hours on Diablo to make the journey to Riga. They made it back again in less than one to the bottom of the defile. She had stiffened up after the rest, her calf muscles like boards, her thighs burning. Carlos made no attempt to suggest that she wait at the car while he and the other man went to find Ricardo. They had rigged up a carrying litter of sorts from a blanket and two poles. The Mestizo carried this while his master strode ahead, Lian bringing up the rear.

Rojo was not far from where she had left him, standing within the shelter of the rocks. The foreleg was still swollen, she noted in passing. He would have to be left, and someone sent out on horseback to fetch him in slowly. They found Ricardo barely conscious, lying on the blankets she had spread for him, the bandage stiff with blood. The sight of his brother stirred him to some semblance of life, his eyes taking on the glint of enmity.

'*You!*' he croaked. 'Why are *you* here?'

'Because your wife came for me,' returned the other. 'Because she and Isabella would not let me refuse to come to you.' He dropped to his knees beside the crumpled blankets and looked into the drawn features for a moment without speaking. Watching them, Lian could suddenly see the resemblance in bone structure; the same set of mouth and jaw. She went to crouch at Carlos's side, her hand going out to touch that of her husband.

'Ricardo, we have a car at the foot of the trail. Carlos and Manuel are going to carry you down to it.'

'You were to go to Mendoza,' he murmured, eyes already glazing again. 'You had no right to defy me.'

'I had no time for considering your difference. Riga was nearer. That was all I cared about.' She kept her voice level. 'And you shouldn't try to talk. You must stay quiet.'

The smile was barely perceptible, his glance towards his

brother ironical. 'What would you do with a woman such as this?'

'I would cherish her,' the other said without change of expression. 'And thank God for such devotion. Lian is right, you should not talk. Be quiet now while we put you on to the litter.'

It took time to get back to where they had left the car. Rojo followed them down, picking his way on three good legs with the injured one barely touching the ground. Ricardo only saw him when they set the litter down in order to open up the tailgate of the car, his brows contracting.

'You—rode—Diablo?' he asked with his eyes on Lian's face. 'You might have been—killed!'

'I had no choice. Rojo was lame.' She waited until the litter had been slid into the car on top of the mattress, then climbed in after it, finding herself a space to huddle with legs curled under her. Ricardo watched her with an expression that mingled emotions unreadably.

'I shall deal with you the very first moment I am able,' he said with a glimmer of humour. 'You knew I would forbid you to ride the stallion.'

'I knew you would worry about my riding him, that's why I didn't tell you.' Lian could smile now at the memory. 'He is headstrong, like his master, but we came to terms. I didn't fall off him once.'

'Which is more than I can say for myself,' on a sudden rueful note. 'I had my mind on other matters.'

'It was all Rojo's fault,' she said quickly. 'Or mine for failing to control him properly. Won't you please stop talking, Ricardo! You need all your strength for the journey back to Mendoza.'

'Only if you give me your hand,' he said, and held out his own to receive it, sinking back with a sigh to close his eyes. 'Later we will talk.'

Carlos said little during the ride. There was something in the set of his shoulders that seemed even harder than before.

Darkness had fallen by the time they came in sight of Mendoza. Ricardo was sleeping, whether naturally or not Lian had no way of judging. His breathing seemed heavy, but then it would in the close confines of the car.

They had been accompanied for the last few miles by a small party of *gauchos*, with José in the lead. The latter had pulled the car up to discover its business here on the Estancia, and insisted on following them in on realising who it was in the back. Several of them came to assist in the removal of the litter from the car, almost fighting for the privilege of helping their employer in his hour of need.

Ricardo opened his eyes again as Inez came bustling from the house wringing her hands in concern and dismay, and spoke to her sharply in her own language. The sleep seemed to have done him good. There was new warmth in the formerly bloodless face. He was even able to prop himself up on an elbow.

Carlos made no attempt to get out of the car. Lian went to where he sat, looking at him through the wound down window with diffidence and uncertainty.

'Won't you come indoors?' she asked.

He shook his head. 'This is as far as I am willing to come. Mendoza is no longer my home.'

'It could be,' she insisted. 'It could be home for all of us if you and Ricardo would only talk things out.'

His expression showed no sign of relenting. 'I have done as you asked and that is enough. Riga is my life now.' He gave the signal to start the engine again, added without looking at her, 'But you are welcome to come and visit with Isabella if you wish it. She has need of a woman friend such as yourself.'

'And Ricardo?'

'I think you will find,' he said, 'that Ricardo still shares my feelings on the matter. We can never be friends, no matter how much you and my wife desire it. Go now to your husband. He will be looking for you.'

It was hopeless, Lian had to concede. She followed the litter party indoors, moving forward to Ricardo's side as they mounted the wide staircase.

'How do you feel?' she asked anxiously.

'Strong enough to reach my bed without being carried there,' came the disgusted reply. 'A bath is all I need to restore me.'

'It is not,' she said firmly. 'A doctor was sent for from Riga. He should be here any time. You're staying quiet and still in bed until he's seen you.'

There was much of the old Ricardo in the look he gave her. 'You press your fortune too far, as the Americans would say. Do not tell me what I shall or shall not do. I will decide that for myself.'

It was on the tip of her tongue to respond in kind when she had a sudden picture of Isabella's remonstrating smile. She paused, letting the light of battle fade from her eyes. 'Yes, Ricardo,' she said demurely, and heard his laugh with a lift of her heart.

'Now I *know* I am concussed!' he said.

The doctor arrived from Santina almost before there was time to get Ricardo on to the big double bed in the room Lian had never before entered. He was a man in his middle years who obviously knew Ricardo well, for he wasted no time on formalities. Hot water was fetched and the filthy bandages removed. Lian watched with anxious heart as he examined first the area of the injury and then shone a pencil beam of light from a torch into his patient's eyes.

'There is some possible concussion,' he pronounced at last, 'but I think no fracture. You must stay here in bed for at least twenty-four hours, and then we shall see.'

'If there is no fracture there is no reason for me to be here at all,' Ricardo stated. 'Do what you have to do to clean this up, and then I will take my bath.' His eyes sought those of his housekeeper hovering in the background. 'Inez, you will run the water for me, please.'

The doctor threw up his hands as if disclaiming all responsibility, but evidently knew his patient too well to bother trying to argue with him. He left some medicine to be taken in case of difficulty in sleeping, and took himself off downstairs again for refreshment before returning to Santina.

Lian had an arm wound round a corner post of the canopied bed, almost as if for support. Meeting the dark gaze as Ricardo swung his legs slowly and somewhat carefully to the floor, she became conscious for the first time of her own appearance, her clothing stained and grubby, her hair wild about a face she was glad she couldn't see.

'I must go and get cleaned up myself,' she said quickly. 'Are you sure you're going to be all right?'

'You wish to stay and make certain?' he asked with familiar satire. 'My bath is large enough for the two of us.' He watched the colour rise under her skin and made a small gesture of appeasement. 'I'm sorry, chica, that was unfair of me. You cannot help the way you are any more than I can myself. Go and change, and then come back. We have much to say to one another.'

Such as? she wondered disconsolately as she went to do as he suggested. The euphoria which had carried her through the greater part of this long day had given way to depression. Loving Ricardo wasn't enough unless he loved her back. She bore his name; she would one day bear his son, but he would never feel for her the way she knew now she felt for him. He had made that so terribly clear last night.

So where was the use in self-pity? she asked herself sharply. She couldn't force him to love her, but what she could do was as he had said and make the most of what they did have. Marriages had succeeded on less.

It was only when she undressed that she realised the full extent of her own injuries. Diablo's saddle had rubbed both thighs into raw red patches covering an area some six to eight inches in diameter. The warm water stung and smarted when she immersed herself in the bath, but she forced herself to bear it. Afterwards she smoothed antiseptic lotion into the patches and tried to forget about them. It was a small price to pay for the ride.

Ricardo was wearing dark slacks and shirt when she went back to his room as he had bidden her, the dressing at his temple standing out whitely against the olive of his skin. He looked tired and drawn but not about to give in.

'I like that,' he said, viewing her long cotton skirt and matching shirt-blouse. 'You haven't worn it before.'

'No.' She stood just within the doorway uncertainly. 'You said you wanted to talk.'

'I said we must both of us talk.' He seemed to be waiting for something, his eyes searching her face, then he sighed and held out his hands. 'Come here to me, Lian.'

She obeyed, putting her hands into his and allowing him to draw her close. His lips were tender on hers, devoid of any demands, his touch light as he held up her face.

'You have courage as well as spirit,' he said softly. 'I owe you my gratitude.'

'I only did what any wife would do for her husband,' she denied, and hesitated before taking the plunge. 'Are you still angry with me for going to Riga?'

'Not angry. Perhaps a little regretful. You have placed me in Carlos's debt.'

'Then I must ask Isabella to arrange an accident for Carlos so that *you* may rescue *him*. Then you'll be even again.'

His expression underwent a change, eyes narrowing. 'I think you mock me,' he said. 'Lian, grateful as I am, I will not allow you to interfere in matters which do not concern you.'

She refused to back down now. 'It has to concern me,' she said with intensity. 'I'm your wife, Ricardo—as Isabella is Carlos's. For her sake, if not for mine, can't you find it in you to bury this feud of yours with Carlos? He doesn't want Mendoza now—he said so.'

'Of course he would say so. He knows there is no chance

of it coming to him now.' His tone held more than a hint of intolerance. 'I am not going to argue with you about this. It is entirely between Carlos and me. As for Isabella——' he stopped and shrugged—'she made her choice, she must live with it.'

'You loved her yourself.' It was out before she could stop it, torn from her by force. 'You hate Carlos because he took her from you!'

'I hated him long before that.' A muscle jerked in the lean jaw as his teeth came together. 'You know nothing about it.'

'Then tell me. *Make* me understand!'

He looked at her for a long tense moment, eyes hard and angry. Then abruptly he turned away from her towards the windows, throwing open the doors to the balcony and standing there with his back to her.

Lian made a tentative movement to follow him. 'Ricardo——'

'No,' he said. 'Stay there. You are right. How can I expect you to understand?' His voice was devoid of expression. 'You already have a very good idea of how I felt about my father, of course. From the time I was first old enough to realise the kind of man he was I detested him with all my heart. He was handsome, and possessed of great charm when it moved him, and he saw no reason to forgo every pleasure life could be made to afford through the use of those attributes. His women were legend; he even brought them here to Mendoza in the guise of house guests along with others to give the semblance of a party. My mother was aware of his unfaithfulness, and he knew it, but still didn't care. He was a man totally without honour.'

She said numbly, 'You don't have to tell me any more, Ricardo. I shouldn't have asked.'

'It has to be said.' He moved his head towards her a little, his features austere. 'You are going to hear all of it. Why my mother continued to love him I cannot say. Women appear to use little reason in their emotional commitments. But love him she did—and it killed her. I watched her change from the beautiful, lighthearted, life-loving creature I knew as a child to a pale, unhappy and thoroughly beaten old woman long before it was time for her to be old. Oh, he was never openly cruel to her, I will grant him that. He would even take the trouble to pay her attentions, when there was no other novelty around to take his interest. He used her when it suited him, then cast her aside the moment he found other amusement.'

'Couldn't she have left him?' Lian asked low-toned. 'Taken you with her and simply walked out?'

'That is what you might do in similar circumstances; it was not in her to take such a step. Neither is it so easy for a woman here in Argentina to leave her husband.'

'But you said she had money of her own.'

'Money, yes—the ability to fend for herself, no. It had never been necessary for her to learn. And remember she still loved my father. Enough, perhaps, to hope that one day he might give up his philandering and come back to her for good. Unfortunately she did not live long enough to find out. A bare month after her death Carlos came to live at Mendoza.'

'And *his* mother?'

His lips twisted. 'No. Even my father had certain principles of conduct. He set her up in Santina and visited her there when he needed her, but only in return for all rights to Carlos.'

'Why would he need another son when he already had a legitimate one?'

'He knew how I felt towards him—I made no secret of my feelings. He would have sent me away from Mendoza, except that it gave him satisfaction to make me live in the same house as my half-brother and taunt me with his intention of making Carlos his heir. There was no doubt that Carlos was his son; they were very alike, both in looks and in ways. Between them they did their best to make me go of my own accord. That way no one could say I had been robbed of my birthright. Only I was equally determined not to go.'

Lian tried to imagine the kind of life it must have been, and felt tears prickle at the back of her eyes. No wonder Ricardo was difficult to reach!

'I don't blame you,' she said. 'I would have done the same.'

'I'm sure you would.' The smile was faint. 'You would spit in the eye of any adversity if it moved you to do so. It was for your spirit that I chose you to help me keep Mendoza.'

'And because you were desperate with time running out.'

'That too. Fortune was on my side in sending me to the Club Rios on the one night when help was to hand.' He paused briefly, studying her face with an odd look in his eyes. 'Does what I've told you help you to appreciate why I find it so difficult to be beholden to Carlos?'

'It goes a long way.'

'But you still believe I should take steps to end our enmity, despite all of it.'

She made a small helpless gesture with her hands. 'Can any of it change what already happened? It was your father who set you against one another. If you both keep it up, he's won, hasn't he?'

Mouth and eyes hardened again. 'No,' he said harshly, 'he hasn't won. I have Mendoza.'

And Carlos had Isabella. It didn't need saying; it was there in his face.

'He loves her,' Lian said painfully. 'I'm sure of it. Perhaps initially he only wanted her because you did, but it's different now.'

'For her sake I hope so.' He looked back over the court-yard, hands in pockets, jaw set. 'Tomorrow we will move across to the other wing. For tonight you will sleep in here with me.'

'Your head——' she began, and heard his jarring laugh.

'My head will feel no worse for holding you in my arms.

I doubt myself fit for anything more than that.' He didn't turn, but there was a subtle change in his tone. 'I want you with me, Lian. Would you deny me so little?'

Her throat hurt. He wanted her with him to stop him thinking about Isabella, the girl he had loved and lost; the girl he would have married had his brother not stolen her heart. She had known something of his feelings for her before, of course, but that didn't allay the pain here and now. Yet what real difference did it make? Nothing had changed. She could provide him with all that he needed now in a wife, and even gain pleasure from it herself. Some would consider her fortunate to have that much.

'I won't deny you anything,' she said on a husky note. 'It's too late, isn't it? Shall I send for some food?'

'No, we will go down for it.' He turned back into the room again, features controlled. 'We both of us need a good stiff drink.'

Alcohol was probably the last thing he should be having, but it was useless to tell him so. He would go his own way if he killed himself doing it. Yet had he been different would she have loved him more? Whatever his faults, they were a part of him, and he was now a part of her. Nothing could change that.

CHAPTER TWELVE

Rojo was brought back little the worse for his prolonged sojourn. The swelling was already going down, although the lameness still prevailed. He would be all right again in a few days' time, Pedro assured Lian when she expressed her concern. There was bruising but no break. All he needed was rest.

One of the Riga hands brought Diablo over on the leading rein during the morning. The stallion seemed fully himself again, snorting his disgust at the indignity of being towed so far behind an inferior animal. Ricardo came out to look him over, calming the restless movements with softly spoken words and the touch of his hands on the glossy black neck. There were half healed scratches on the side which had taken the brunt of the fall. He looked at them, ran his hands over all four legs and seemed satisfied that all was reasonably well.

'Come over and say hallo to him,' he said to Lian, who was watching. 'I wish to see how he reacts now to the first woman to master him.'

Not quite the first, she thought as she went tentatively to obey. The stallion watched her coming with a suspicious eye, jerking his head as she put out a hand to his nose, then standing still apart from a quivering in his flanks while she ran the hand up and over his neck and shoulder.

'Do you want to try mounting him again?' Ricardo asked without revealing any particular reaction.

She shook her head. 'I don't think so. Yesterday was a special occasion. He prefers your hands on him.'

His smile flickered briefly. 'He is not, I hope, alone in that.' He despatched the stallion into his stall and fastened across the bar before adding, 'Do your legs still pain you this morning?'

'Not nearly as much.' Lian tried to sound matter-of-fact about it. 'Thanks to your ministrations.'

'Which you would rather have gone without.' There was a gleam of sardonic amusement in his eyes when he turned. 'If I hadn't heard you cry out when you moved in the night I would have been no wiser, eh? One of these days you will lose this self-consciousness with me. There is nothing which cannot be shared between husband and wife. Tell me, had my injuries been of a nature which necessitated the removal of my clothing, would you have allowed me to bleed to death rather than suffer such embarrassment?'

'You don't have to mock me,' she retorted with some spirit. 'Men have a different attitude, that's all.'

'That is not answering my question.'

She sighed. 'No, of course I wouldn't have let you bleed to death. That's ridiculous!'

'I am relieved.' He looked at her and softened a little, catching her arm and drawing her closer. 'You are right, I should not tease you. Your attitude will change in time.'

'As we become more familiar?' Her tone was deliberately light. 'Doesn't that breed contempt?'

'It had better not,' he said. 'I will have no wife of mine show me contempt.' His hold on her firmed along with the line of his jaw. 'We are going to be married a long time, little one—you can settle your mind to that. It might not be all that either of us could have asked for, but it is all we have and we will make the best we can of it. Did you see to the changing of our rooms?'

'Not yet.'

'Then go and do so now. I will have the one with the dressing-room off it.' The mockery was back, although somewhat self-directed this time. 'Not that I expect to be spending too much of my time there.'

Not, at least, until he had fulfilled his object, Lian thought numbly as she left him. Yet why not? If she had Ricardo's child she would have something born of love, even if it was one-sided. It was better than nothing.

That was something she was to tell herself often during the days following. At night, lying in Ricardo's arms, she could even forget the one-sidedness of that love in his passion. In this one respect, if in no other, his need of her was without reserve.

The head wound healed but left a scar which would probably always be with him—his souvenir, he called it in his lighter moments. It wasn't until Lian saw him fingering it one day with a certain look in his eyes that she realised he saw it as a constant reminder of the debt he owed his brother.

The feud with Carlos was the one thing she could never put out of her mind for long. Were they to go through the whole of their lives suffering this estrangement from their closest neighbours? Were she and Isabella condemned to the occasional stolen meeting, instead of being able to visit one another as most sister-in-laws living within reasonably easy reach might do? And what about when children came along —for both sides? They too would become part of the same deadlocked situation. It could carry on for generations unless something were done about it now. But what? There seemed no possible way in which she, or Isabella either for that matter, could intervene.

When a possible solution first suggested itself she refused to regard it with any seriousness at first. Such things might have worked for the ancient Greeks, but she could imagine Ricardo's reaction.

Yet the notion refused to be banished. Impractical it might be, but Aristophanes had made it seem plausibly effective in circumstances not dissimilar to these. Why not here? Yes, but that had been a concerted effort, she reminded herself wryly. One could hardly see Isabella lending herself to such a scheme. She was probably wise at that. There had to be some more reasonable way.

Isabella's visit to Mendoza came as a complete surprise. She arrived by car on a morning when Ricardo was away from the *casa*, relieved to find Lian alone.

'I had to come,' she said. 'Even if it meant facing Ricardo's anger. You and I have need of one another, Lian, if our husbands do not.' A faint smile crossed the lovely features as she refused the coffee Lian offered to send for. 'I would prefer orange juice, if you do not mind.'

'You're having a baby!' It was sheer instinct on Lian's part, prompted more by the bloom the other carried with her than by a simple request for a cool drink. Envy swept through her, though in no way which detracted from her delight for the other girl. 'Oh, I'm so pleased for you! When?'

'Still almost eight months. It is not yet medically confirmed, but I am sure enough in my own mind. A woman knows these things, does she not?'

'I'm sure she does.' Lian could go along with that kind of emotional certainty. 'How does Carlos feel about becoming a father?'

'He is in heaven.' Isabella's brow contracted. 'No, that is not quite true. He would be so were he not distracted by other matters he will not talk about with me. Lian, what are we going to do about our husbands? Can we allow them to continue this stupidity?'

Lian pulled a face. 'Do we have any choice? They've lived with their hatred too long to be persuaded to shake hands just for the asking.'

'*Si*.' Isabella gave a sigh. 'A hatred fostered by a father who loved neither of them.'

'Neither?'

'Of course not. You thought differently?'

Lian hesitated. 'Ricardo thinks differently.'

'Then he is wrong. Ricardo was at least his legitimate child, and could find some comfort in that. Carlos was never once allowed to forget his birth, and had nothing to cling to. Do you not see, their father set them against one another with purpose to see them both suffer. He was a man who found amusement in such things; a sadist in the worst possible way. Each of them believed the other was the favourite. Carlos was just as surprised as Ricardo by the terms of his will.'

'But he was still prepared to accept them.'

'Much against my pleading, yes, he was, if only to prove to Ricardo that he was as much a Mendoza as himself. I was never more thankful than when Ricardo brought you home in time to stop it, although it took me a long time to make Carlos see the rightness of it. He is happy to make his life on Riga now.'

'Only not prepared to tell Ricardo that.'

'Any more than Ricardo would be prepared to believe it. They are both of them intractable.' Isabella paused, her eyes on Lian's face. 'Your language allows much scope for interpretation. Does it also allow you any solution?'

The hesitation was lengthy. It couldn't work, of course, but was it worth a try? 'There is a possible one,' Lian said at last with some reluctance. 'But it would take a lot of nerve.'

'So? Tell me.'

'Did you ever hear of Lysistrata?'

'Not that I recall.'

'She was a lady of ancient Greece who got fed-up with her husband always going off to war and persuaded her fellow grass-widows to join her in doing something about it.'

Isabella laughed. 'I am not at all sure I understand all the words, but I think I have the gist. What did she persuade them to do?'

Lian drew a breath, said levelly, 'To deny their husbands conjugal rights until such time as they agreed to forgo their warring instincts.'

The silence could almost be heard. Isabella's face was a picture. 'You were right when you said it required nerve,' she managed at length. Her nose wrinkled. 'Carlos would be devastated!'

'I know. Ricardo too.' They looked at one another and hastily controlled the smiles.

'You really do love him, do you not?' said Isabella softly. 'I had my doubts in the beginning, but your concern for him when you came to fetch Carlos was more than convincing.'

'It's a long story,' Lian admitted, stifling the inevitable ache. 'We started off badly.' She paused with deliberation. 'Well? What about it?'

The other's expression held uncertainty. 'Do you really think it might work?'

'We won't ever know unless we try it.'

'But dare we? How could we——' she paused delicately —'tell them?'

'From behind a locked door, preferably,' Lian said with dry humour. 'Locked, bolted *and* barred. If we do it at all we must do it together.'

'Where?'

'When might be more to the point.' Recklessness swept suddenly through her. The longer they waited the harder it was going to be. 'What's wrong with now?'

Dark eyes widened. 'You mean today?'

'Yes. What time are you expecting Carlos home?'

'I am not sure. Sometimes he returns for luncheon, not always.'

'But your parents know where you are?'

'Madre does, though I swore her to secrecy.'

'She will have to tell him if you don't go back.' Lian had the bit between her teeth now, refusing to consider the drawbacks. Her own marriage might not be everything it should be, but she could at least attempt to straighten out one more retarding factor. If the thought occurred that she might be using this as a personal retaliation it was pushed to the back of her mind. 'I imagine he'll come over to fetch you post-haste once he knows.'

'And Ricardo?'

'He didn't say either. They might even get here together. By the time they do we'll be barricaded in a room with enough food to see us through a couple of days if necessary.'

'Two *days*!' Isabella sounded dismayed. 'You think it may take so long to get them to agree?'

'I think it may take some time to convince them they're not going to get us out until they do agree. We're going to have to be strong-minded about it once we get started.'

'But what if they break down the door?' Her brows drew together. 'Carlos would be angry enough to do anything!'

Lian smiled. 'He could hardly be too angry with you in your condition.'

'Ah no!' An answering smile lit Isabella's face. 'As an expectant mother I cannot be held responsible for my actions. Everyone knows that pregnancy brings odd impulses!' She sobered again to add seriously, 'But you are not pregnant. Ricardo will beat you!'

'He'll have to reach me first. We'll just have to make sure the door is well blocked. A load of furniture pushed in front of it should do it.'

'And afterwards?' Isabella was warming to the idea despite herself. 'Even if they do agree to stop their fighting are they not still going to be angry when we come out?'

'I expect so.' Lian wished she felt quite so confident as she sounded. 'That's something I'll have to deal with when it comes.' She looked at her watch. 'It's almost half past eleven now. We should make a move right away in case Ricardo comes back early. I'll go and see about getting some food. It will have to be cold, unfortunately, unless we can find a portable stove. Ricardo has one, but I don't know where he keeps it.'

'I think we had better keep things as simple as they can be.' Laughter suddenly gurgled through Isabella's lips. 'I never thought to have a sister such as you, Lian. You are so much more daring than I would ever have dreamed of being!'

Or foolhardy; Lian wasn't sure which. An odd mood had settled on her. Ricardo had had things so much his own way during the time of their acquaintance. If nothing else, this would at least show him he did not have her completely in hand. Love him she might; subjugate herself to that emotion she would not!

The kitchen staff regarded her request for food with astonishment when they realised the amount. Inez, luckily, was not in evidence. Ignoring the speculation, Lian piled as much of a variety as she was able to carry on to a large tray and ordered it taken upstairs to the room she had formely occupied herself, along with several bottles of cordial. There was water on tap in the bathroom adjoining. They had all they needed to withstand quite a siege.

The whole situation had taken on an air of adventure by the time she and Isabella reached the room. Laughing, Lian insisted that the other sit down while she dragged across the most suitable pieces of furniture to block the locked door. The balcony window was more difficult. It took her almost half an hour to manoeuvre a heavy wardrobe across several feet to cover it. The room was darkened by the move, though not uncomfortably so. Finished at last, she flung herself on to the bed cover and looked at Isabella with a grin of triumph.

'Now let them find a way in! Shall we eat lunch?'

The following hour passed with a swiftness that took them both by surprise. Given opportunity for the first time to find points of common interest, they talked until they were tired of talking, sharing backgrounds and childhood memories, laughing over recollections of past misdemeanours. As an only child, Isabella listened with unconcealed envy to Lian's tales of her orphanage days.

'So many playmates,' she kept saying. 'So many brothers and sisters to share with. Oh, Lian, if you only knew how I longed to have lots of other children to play with! Only poor Madre could not. And Santina was so far away.'

'But you came to Mendoza.'

'Oh, yes, often. My father would bring me when he came to play chess with Ricardo's father. Oddly enough, they were not bad friends, although two more different people you could not find. Perhaps Señor Mendoza found little to amuse him in a man who would not respond to provocation of any kind. He has always believed that quarrels are caused by people being too sensitive to imagined insult, so he never allows himself to see one.'

'That's quite a philosophy,' Lian said, and the other girl laughed.

'Oh yes, but it would only work for someone like my father.' She paused, recollecting their reason for being here in this room. 'What time is it?'

'Gone one,' Lian told her, and staved off her own trepidation with another banana. 'Shouldn't be long now.'

It was longer than either of them had anticipated before anything happened. As the afternoon wore on their conversation began to peter out and lose its thread, along with the first enthusiasm of resolve. Isabella was lying on the bed and Lian sitting in a chair, both in complete silence, when the sound of voices reached them from the courtyard below. It was Carlos speaking, his tone abrupt, although the words themselves could not be made out through the closed doors.

They both sat up, Isabella with suddenly apprehensive eyes.

'You think they are both of them here?'

'I don't know,' Lian admitted. 'I can't make out who else was with him.' She firmed her own expression. 'Anyway, we'll soon find out.'

They did. Footsteps sounded along the corridor, and the door handle was turned.

'Lian?' came Ricardo's voice. 'You are in there?'

Lian made a face at Isabella without stirring from her chair. 'Yes,' she answered. 'We're both in here.'

'Then open the door. At once!'

'No,' she said clearly. 'We're staying put.'

There was a momentary pause, a smothered exclamation, and the thud of a fist hitting the panel hard. 'Open this door!' he thundered.

'No!' she was sitting bolt upright now, high spots of colour on her cheekbones, aware of Isabella's wide-eyed stare. 'We're staying right here until you and Carlos give us good reason to come out!'

The lock rattled as he thrust his weight against it, but it held. '*I'll* give you good reason to come out, without Carlos! You have five seconds to get this open before I put my shoulder to it!'

There were two chests of drawers and a tallboy in front of the door. Looking at them now, Lian thought they appeared horribly inadequate.

'Do you think——' Isabella began, and stopped with a faint resigned sigh as green eyes turned fiercely towards her.

'Five,' said Ricardo outside, and they both heard the intake of furiously drawn breath. From the sound of the impact which came almost immediately afterwards, it wasn't his shoulder he was using as a ram but his foot. The wood around the lock splintered and gave, yet by some miracle continued to hold it intact. Lian waited in fascinated suspense for a second attack.

Another voice came to them before that could happen. There was the sound of consultation, and then Carlos's knuckles rapping on the panel.

'Isabella!'

His wife gave a sudden little giggle as she caught Lian's eye, her spirit returning. 'Yes, Carlos?' she called demurely.

The unflurried response seemed to take him aback. Several seconds passed before he said uncertainly, 'What is all this about? Why have you locked yourselves away in there?'

It was Lian who answered because Isabella was obviously at a loss for what to say. 'Is Ricardo still there?' she demanded.

'Yes,' came the measured reply, 'I am here. But not for very much longer, I assure you. This time you have gone too far!'

'I won't take long.' She had planned the words she was going to use; she only hoped they would convey firm resolution. 'In ancient Greece the women had one way of ensuring peace among their menfolk. We'll resume proper marital relations with ours only when you and Carlos agree to forget the past—and start acting like grown men!'

That last came out as an involuntary addition, unrehearsed and, judging from Isabella's expression, overplayed. From the silence outside the whole speech had gone down like a veritable thunderbolt. Ricardo was the first to react, his voice thick with anger.

'Lysistrata and her compatriots had one advantage over you. There were more of them. I don't know what kind of ridiculous game you think you are playing, but it had better stop right here and now!'

'It's no game. We're both sick of the feuding! You won't make the effort yourselves, so we're making it for you. Right, Isabella?'

The dark eyes rolled resignedly, her shoulders lifting. 'Yes.'

'Isabella!' Carlos's voice had lost all belligerence and taken on bewilderment. 'What are you saying? What has happened to you?'

'My wife has happened to her,' Ricardo interposed. 'Lian grows bored with her life and must find some new amusement. You may move Isabella by talking to her through the door. Personally I would not waste the time.' The pause was significant. 'You have one more opportunity to stop this nonsense, Lian. Otherwise I'm coming in to put a stop to it myself. You had no right to involve Isabella in your idiotic schemes in her condition!'

'My condition should contribute to, not detract from our appeal,' said the latter suddenly and unexpectedly. Her cheeks were hot, as if she had been running, her eyes stormy. 'Do you either of you imagine I would wish to bring a child into an environment where his father and his uncle cannot even exchange a civil word? Lian is right when she calls you children. In fact, she does not go far enough. I would add vindictive!'

In the stunned silence which followed her outburst she put a hand up quickly to her mouth as if in horrified realisation of what she had said, meeting Lian's widened gaze with eyes that mirrored the same astonishment.

'*Madre de dios!*' she breathed.

This time it was Carlos who was first to speak. He sounded like a man faced with something outside his comprehension; dazed and uncertain. 'Isabella,' he said softly. '*Chica mia*, I did not know you felt like this! Please open the door and come out. We will talk, Ricardo and I. You have my word.'

Slowly the astonishment faded from Isabella's face to be replaced by a smile. With her eyes still on Lian, she called, 'Ricardo, you agree?'

The answer came after another long moment. 'We will talk.'

Even he sounded subdued, Lian thought. The gentle Isabella had astounded them all with the ferocity of her attack. She got to her feet and went to move the furniture away from the door, opening it and looking at the two men standing outside without expression.

Carlos pressed past her to go to his wife still sitting on the bed. Without speaking, Ricardo put out a hand and drew her from the doorway, turning her roughly along the corridor towards the room he himself had previously occupied.

The shutters were closed over the balcony windows, slatting the light filtering through them and lending an odd green cast to the olive of his features. There was a crossfire of emotions in his regard.

'Why?' he demanded. 'Why did you do this? It was your idea, was it not?'

She wet her lips, aware of the hard lump in her throat, 'Yes,' she said. 'It was my idea. I persuaded Isabella to do it.' The pause was brief. 'Did you mean what you said when you agreed to talk things over with Carlos?'

'What other choice did I have under the circumstances? What choice did either of us have?' His mouth was compressed. 'Isabella is in no fit state to be agitated the way she was. I could hurt you for that alone!'

Her shrug was deliberate. 'Go ahead if it makes you feel any better. I'll take my punishment like a big girl.'

'Like an adult?' There were tawny sparks in the depths of his eyes. 'A grown woman!'

'Oh, stop it,' she said wearily. 'What's the use of going over it? All right, so I went too far. It was a rotten idea. You and Carlos aren't going to make things up. It's too late. I should have know all along it was too late!'

He was quiet for what seemed like an age looking at her. 'Why was it so important to you?' he said at last. 'What does it matter whether Carlos and I are friends or enemies? Does it change anything between us? Would it make you look at me with fresh eyes?' His tone was cool and level. 'I have a wife, why should I need a brother? You give me all a man could ever desire in life, *querida*—your beautiful body, mine to hold and caress whenever I wish, your lovely face to look at, your hair to run my fingers through. We have so much, you and I. We will have even more when you bear me my son. Are you not satisfied with your lot?'

'No,' she said. 'I'm not satisfied.' Her head was lifted, her voice impassioned. 'You think that's all it takes to create a marriage—two people and a bed. You really believe physical compatibility is enough? Well, it may be for you, but I happen to have other ideas. You asked me once a long time ago if I envied Isabella the attentions of a man like Carlos and I told you not to be ridiculous. You were right to be angry then, because you weren't being ridiculous. Not one little bit!' She was trembling now and unable to conceal it, her whole body quivering with the need to reach out and hurt him as he had hurt her. 'I envied Isabella then and I envy her now, because she has a man who knows what love really is. And I'll tell you something else for what it's worth to you. If you had married her yourself she would never have known the kind of happiness she knows now, because *you* don't know *how* to love! You're cold and calculating and h-heartless and——' she broke off in sudden surrender to the emotion choking her. 'Oh, go away,' she got out in husky appeal. 'Leave me alone!'

'Lian.' His voice was soft with shock. 'Oh, my God, Lian!' His hands were cupping her face, lifting it so that he could look into it, his eyes searching hers with an expression that shook her. 'Are you trying to tell me you want my love as much as I want yours? Is that what this is all about?'

The house was still with the afternoon hush, her heartbeats the only sound she could hear with any clarity.

'You told me only a week ago that you loved Isabella,' she whispered at last.

'Yes, I loved her.' His fingers tightened a fraction as he felt her start to pull away. 'I have known her and loved her from a child, and as naturally accepted that one day I would make her my wife. It was only after Carlos had taken her, and forced me to find means of retaining Mendoza, that I began to realise there could be other kinds of love. What I felt for Isabella was gentle and good and would have subscribed to a contented marriage. What I feel for you——' he paused, registering the growing light and warmth in her eyes with comprehension and release—'what I feel for you in as different as storm from calm. You anger me, you torment me, you rouse me to passion and to fury; yet through it all I continue to want you as I have wanted no other woman in my life, to love you to distraction in the hope that one day you will return my emotion.' His hands had moved from her face to her shoulders, lifting her up to him, his whole face alive with the realisation of that hope fulfilled. 'Lian——'

She put her arms about his neck and her lips to his in swift and complete surrender, not trying to work things out for now, content just to know.

'Oh, Ricardo,' she breathed against the strong brown cheek when he held her to him.

'Oh, Ricardo!' he mocked, but there was tenderness in his voice. 'You sound like some fugitive from a romantic novel!'

'I feel like one too.' She laughed softly. 'And you're not going to pull me back down to earth that easily either. Tell me when you knew you loved me.'

He groaned. 'How like a woman to ask such a question! How do I know just when? There was no one time when I stopped and said it to myself. It came upon me gradually.'

'Against your will?'

'Perhaps. My will has undergone a great deal of strain these last weeks.'

'It hasn't been noticeable.' Her hand was in his hair, running the thick blackness between her fingers as she had longed to do on so many other occasions. 'I can still hardly take it in. Only bare moments ago I was so depressed and unhappy, hating you almost. And now——'

'And now?' he prompted as she broke off. He was smiling as she had never seen him smile before, with no trace of irony or satire in the curve of his lips. 'What do you feel now, *amada mia*?'

'Like a cat that's been given a saucer of cream,' she responded with an answering sparkle. 'Ready to purr!'

'And no doubt to scratch again the moment the cream is

forgotten.' He ran his hands possessively along her bare arms, moulding the line of her collarbone between strong fingers. 'There was a time when I so badly desired to draw those sharp little claws of yours. I am glad now that I found it so difficult. Life would be lacking in variety were it not for your indomitable spirit. You keep me constantly on my toes.'

'That can't be comfortable.'

'Comfort I can do without. *You* are what I need; just as you are. My own English rebel!' His eyes darkened, glinting with familiar lights. 'We have much to make up for. To hold you in my arms and know there is love in your heart will fill my cup to overflowing. Will you come to our bed with me now and let me taste that delight?'

'I want to,' she said with honesty. 'You can't imagine how *much* I want to. But we can't, not yet. How can we leave Isabella and Carlos at a time like this?'

'I had forgotten them,' he confessed. 'I had forgotten everything but our two selves.' He pulled her up to him and kissed her again with passion and with need, releasing her with reluctance and obvious regret. 'What you did this afternoon, you and Isabella, was reprehensible but perhaps merited. You were right in what you said of us—vindictive *and* less than adult. Carlos and I have taken pleasure in our hatred of one another; fostered it even. It will not be easy for either of us to extend the hand of friendship, but for you and for Isabella I think we must try.'

'Now?'

'The sooner the better. But later, when we are alone again, then I will love my wife.' His smile was slow, his hand at her nape like a promise. 'We have a son to make, little one —a new Argentinian. I hope he will have his mother's eyes.'

ROMANCE

Variety is the spice of romance

Each month, Mills & Boon publish new romances. New stories about people falling in love. A world of variety in romance – from the best writers in the romantic world. Choose from these titles in November.

CHAINS OF REGRET Margaret Pargeter
BELOVED STRANGER Elizabeth Oldfield
SUBTLE REVENGE Carole Mortimer
MARRIAGE UNDER FIRE Daphne Clair
A BAD ENEMY Sara Craven
SAVAGE ATONEMENT Penny Jordan
A SECRET INTIMACY Charlotte Lamb
GENTLE PERSUASION Claudia Jameson
THE FACE OF THE STRANGER Angela Carson
THE TYZAK INHERITANCE Nicola West
TETHERED LIBERTY Jessica Steele
NO OTHER CHANCE Avery Thorne

On sale where you buy paperbacks. If you require further information or have any difficulty obtaining them, write to: Mills & Boon Reader Service, PO Box 236, Thornton Road, Croydon, Surrey CR9 3RU, England.

Mills & Boon
the rose of romance

Best Seller Romances

Romances you have loved

Mills & Boon Best Seller Romances are the love stories that have proved particularly popular with our readers. They really are "back by popular demand." These are the six titles to look out for this month.

UNWANTED BRIDE
by Anne Hampson

The last time Caryn had seen her husband Sharn was at their wedding – a marriage of convenience so that both could claim an inheritance. But now she needed help and journeyed to Sharn's Outback home. Surely he wouldn't refuse to assist Caryn? Yet Sharn had told nobody about his wife and didn't seem at all willing to take on his responsibilities as a husband!

NIGHT OF THE YELLOW MOON
by Flora Kidd

Delia's marriage to Edmund had run into trouble almost as soon as it had begun – but was an expedition in the depths of the Brazilian jungle the best place to try and sort things out – especially as Edmund hadn't wanted her to come in the first place!

Mills & Boon

HAWK IN A BLUE SKY
by Charlotte Lamb

was five years since Amanda had turned down Cesare's proposal
marriage, but now she was going back again to his home in
scany – this time engaged to his younger brother Piero. And it
on became clear that Cesare was not going to accept the new
uation any more than he had accepted the old. But what could
manda do about it?

THE WRONG MAN TO LOVE
by Roberta Leigh

mantha supposed her beloved godfather had known what he
s doing when he left her the controlling shares in his huge
partment store – but how she wished he hadn't done it! For all it
l to was her falling in love with Zachary Farrell, the new head of
e business – who naturally had no time for her at all!

LORD OF LA PAMPA
by Kay Thorpe

hen Lian was stranded in Buenos Aires Ricardo Mendoza
scued her from a very dangerous predicament – and thereby put
r in his debt. But it seemed there was a way she could repay him –
becoming his wife, in name only, for the next six months. It
emed little enough to commit herself to in the circumstances,
t . . .

THE LOVED AND THE FEARED
by Violet Winspear

e world-famous film star Serafina Neri made slaves of the men
o surrounded her – even her spoilt son Adone – so what was
ung Donna Lovelace to do when she fell in love with Rick
rdetti, who seemed to be at Serafina's beck and call day
d night?

the rose of romance

How to join in a whole new world of romance

It's very easy to subscribe to the Mills & Boon Reader Service. As a regular reader, you can enjoy a whole range of special benefits. Bargain offers. Big cash savings. Your own free Reader Service newsletter, packed with knitting patterns, recipes, competitions, and exclusive book offers.

We send you the very latest titles each month, postage and packing free – no hidden extra charges. There's absolutely no commitment – you receive books for only as long as you want.

We'll send you details. Simply send the coupon – or drop us a line for details about the Mills & Boon Reader Service Subscription Scheme. Post to: Mills & Boon Reader Service, P.O. Box 236, Thornton Road, Croydon, Surrey CR9 3RU, England. *Please note: READERS IN SOUTH AFRICA please write to: Mills & Boon Reader Service of Southern Africa, Private Bag X3010, Randburg 2125, S. Africa.

Please send me details of the Mills & Boon Subscription Scheme.

NAME (Mrs/Miss) _____ EP3

ADDRESS_____

_____

COUNTY/COUNTRY_____ POST/ZIP CODE_____

BLOCK LETTERS, PLEASE

Mills & Boon
the rose of romance